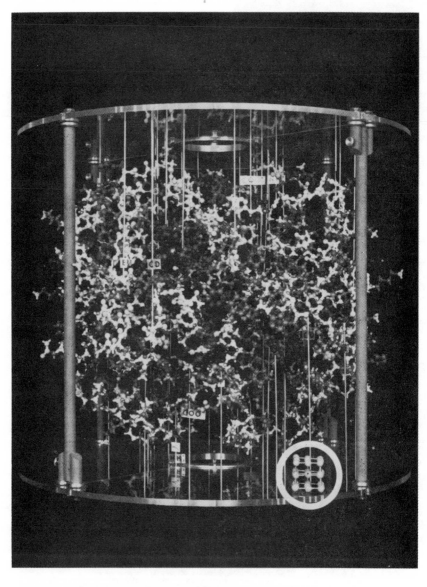

X-Ray Structure Analysis: 1913–68.
The molecular structure of haemoglobin, as determined by M. F. Perutz and his colleagues, compared with the unit-cell of rock salt (inset) to the same scale.

The Development of X-ray Analysis

SIR LAWRENCE BRAGG
C.H., F.R.S.

Edited by:

D.C. Phillips, F.R.S.

Professor of Molecular Biophysics,
University of Oxford

and

H. Lipson, F.R.S.

University of Manchester,
Institute of Science and Technology

DOVER PUBLICATIONS, INC.
New York

Published in Canada by General Publishing Company, Ltd., 30 Lesmill
Road, Don Mills, Toronto, Ontario.
Published in the United Kingdom by Constable and Company, Ltd., 3 The
Lanchesters, 162–164 Fulham Palace Road, London W6 9ER.

This Dover edition, first published in 1992, is an unabridged and corrected
republication of the edition first published by G. Bell and Sons, Ltd.,
London, in 1975. A new foreword to the Dover edition has been written by
S.L. Bragg.

Manufactured in the United States of America
Dover Publications, Inc., 31 East 2nd Street, Mineola, New York 11501

Library of Congress Cataloging-in-Publication Data

Bragg, William Lawrence, Sir, 1890–1971.
    The development of x-ray analysis / Sir Lawrence Bragg ; edited by D.C.
Phillips and H. Lipson.
       p.   cm.
    Originally published : London, G. Bell, 1975.
    Includes bibliographical references and index.
    ISBN 0-486-67316-2
    1. X-ray crystallography.   I. Phillips. D.C. (David C.)   II. Lipson, H.
(Henry), 1910–1991.   III. Title.
QD945.B688   1975b
548′.83—dc20   92-39217
                                                      CIP

FOREWORD TO THE 1975 EDITION

My father planned this book as an overall review of the subject of X-ray analysis, which had been the centre of his life's work as a physicist. He discussed the plan with Professor David Phillips, who had worked with him at the Royal Institution during an exciting phase of the development: and he had always intended to rely on Phillips for comment and for help with certain material.

In the event, the basic manuscript was completed only two weeks before W.L.B.'s death, on 1 July 1971. David Phillips immediately took over the burden of completing the work, which involved some rearrangement of the later chapters, revision of drawings and diagrams and all the essential but tedious chores of checking and proof reading. He was ably assisted in this by Professor Henry Lipson, who had worked with W.L.B. in Manchester.

They undertook this work as a labour of love and on behalf of the Bragg family I would like to record our deep gratitude to them for ensuring that this book should be a fitting memorial to the founder of X-ray analysis.

We would also like to thank the Trustees of the Leverhulme Fund for defraying the costs of preparing the manuscript: finally I know that W.L.B. would have wanted to express his warmest thanks to Mrs. Corinne Wakefield and Mrs. Brenda Wayne for their loyal help in typing the text and drawing the figures.

S. L. Bragg

AKNOWLEDGMENTS

The publisher and editors wish to thank the following for permission to reproduce illustrations.

The Science Museum: Fig. 1.1.

Longman Group Limited: Figs. 1.2; 1.3; 8.5(*a*).

Van Nostrand Reinhold Co. Ltd., New York: Fig. 1.5.

The Royal Society: Figs. 2.11.(*a–c*); 2.12; 3.1; 3.3; 3.4; 3.5; 5.11; 5.2; 9.10(*b*); 15.7; 15.10.

Philosophical Magazine: Figs. 3.6; 3.7; 3.8; 4.1; 4.2; 4.3; 4.4;

Nobel Foundation: Figs. 9.6; 15.11.

The Chemical Society, *Journal of the Chemical Society*: Fig. 9.8.

Progress in the Chemistry of Organic Natural Products, Vol. XV: Fig. 9.12;

Oxford University Press: Figs. 15.2; 15.3.

Friedr. Vieweg & Sohn, GmBH., *Advances in Structure Research*, Vol. 2; Fig. 15.4.

FOREWORD TO THE DOVER EDITION

I was delighted when Dover Publications undertook to reprint my father's comprehensive history of the development of X-ray analysis. Once again we are deeply indebted to Sir David Phillips, now Emeritus Professor of Molecular Biophysics in the University of Oxford, for meticulously collecting and checking comments and queries that had been raised by readers of the first edition, which he had edited with the late Professor Henry Lipson. He has only found it necessary to make a few small corrections in the text.

S.L. Bragg

INTRODUCTION

This book does not claim to be a complete and up-to-date account of all the progress now being made in X-ray analysis in laboratories over the world. It is of a more historical and reminiscent nature. In describing each new advance I have chosen my examples and illustrations from the first work which broke new ground, rather than from the latest achievements. I have tried to see these advances in perspective, and recall the excitement and enthusiasm at the time as each new insight into the structure of matter was achieved, over the sixty years since X-ray analysis started.

The subject divides naturally into two main sections. The first concerns the 'Art of X-ray Analysis'. The principles of physical optics which are used to deduce the atomic arrangement from observations of diffraction are classical and well-known, but owing to the importance of the quest they have been intensively developed. Many refinements of treatment have been devised which make it possible to analyse ever more complex structures. Ingenious automatic apparatus has been developed for dealing with vast numbers of measurements, and these measurements are handled by computers. This side of X-ray analysis is pure Physics.

The other aspect is the interpretation of the significance of the results, and here many other sciences are involved, such as chemistry, mineralogy, metallurgy, biochemistry, physiology, and genetics. From the viewpoints of these sciences, X-ray analysis is a tool; it is in the results that the interest lies. The first part of this book deals with analysis, the second with results.

I have tried to put into this book the ways of treating the problems, the examples, and the homely analogies, which I have personally found effective in my lecturing experience. I think that the illustrations from the earliest work have some advantage in being more simple and more readily grasped than the complex story of the latest advances. I hope, too, that some of the examples and illustrations will be useful to those who teach this fascinating subject.

W. L. Bragg
1971

CONTENTS

CHAPTER 1

RÖNTGEN RAYS

1. The Discovery of X-rays

In 1895 W. C. Röntgen in Germany made one of those great discoveries which change profoundly a whole branch of science. He found a new type of radiation coming from a discharge tube which, because of its mysterious nature, he termed X-rays. He noticed that a screen coated with barium platino-cyanide fluoresced in the neighbourhood of the tube when a discharge was passing, even when a shield opaque to light was placed between the tube and the screen and he traced the effect to rays coming from a place on the wall of the discharge tube, opposite to the cathode or negative terminal, which showed a greenish glow when the tube was highly exhausted. It was known that the glow was due to some kind of radiation coming from the cathode (the cathode rays) because an obstacle placed in the path threw a shadow on the glass of the tube. These cathode rays were of course later identified by J. J. Thomson as the electrons, or corpuscles as he called them, which were repelled by the cathode owing to their negative charge, were shot across the evacuated tube, and hit the glass on the far side. It was later found convenient to place a platinum plate (the anticathode) in the path of the cathode rays which then became the source of the X-rays, and to focus the electron beam on the plate by making the cathode concave. Two early types of X-ray tubes are shown in Fig. 1.

The rays followed straight lines like light and obstacles placed in their path cast shadows. As well as making screens fluoresce, they affected photographic plates. Indeed, other observers had previously noticed that photographic plates kept in the neighbourhood of a discharge tube became fogged although in a light-tight wrapping, but they had missed the significance of the effect.

Röntgen studied the absorption of these rays in matter, and found that it followed laws in striking contrast to those governing the absorp-

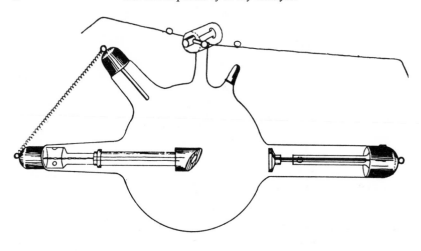

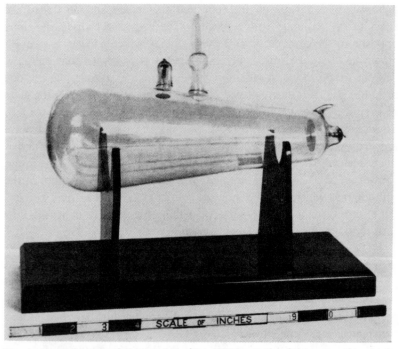

FIG. 1. An early type of X-ray tube with cathode on the right and anti-cathode at the centre.

tion of light: the absorbing power depended only on the kinds of atom in the absorbing screen. Bodies such as paper or wood, made of light atoms, were very transparent; for instance he could observe the fluorescence through a book with 1000 pages! On the other hand quite thin sheets of heavy metals were very absorbing. The flesh of our bodies is transparent since it is almost entirely composed of carbon, nitrogen, oxygen and hydrogen whereas the bones are opaque because they contain calcium. A photograph of a hand taken by Röntgen is shown in Fig. 2. This property of the X-rays was immediately exploited by the medical world as X-ray radiography, for examining fractures or locating the position of foreign bodies such as objects accidentally swallowed or bullets.

Another property of the radiation uncovered at this time proved to be of the greatest scientific importance; the rays made a gas a conductor of electricity. As we would now put it, the rays 'ionized' the gas by making the molecules acquire positive and negative charges which enabled an electric current to flow.

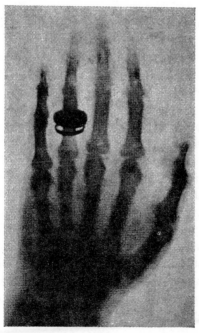

FIG. 2. An early X-ray photograph of a hand taken by Röntgen in 1895. The rings show up as dark shadows because they are made of highly absorbing material.

An English translation of Röntgen's original paper Ueber eine neue Art von Strahlen was published in *Nature* (1896). The student who is interested is warmly advised to consult this account. As is so often the case in original papers, one is struck by the breadth of first surveys; many of the properties of X-rays which are generally regarded as having been discovered in subsequent work by others are foreshadowed.

Among scientists there was much speculation as to whether the X-rays were another form of light, or whether they were some new and strange type of radiation.

2. The Wave Theory of Light

The wave nature of light had been regarded since the beginning of the nineteenth century as established by Young's experiments on interference. Young used sunlight coming through a pinhole in a screen as a source, which illuminated two pinholes close together in a second screen. Young observed that when the light from these pinholes fell in turn upon a third screen, the path of light is crossed by a system of 'fringes', or parallel light and dark bands.

Young's explanation of the effect is well illustrated by his own diagram, shown in Fig. 3. Where the waves overlap, crests and troughs coincide at some places where their effects add, and cut each other out at intermediate places, so producing the light and dark fringes. This is known as the principle of 'Interference'. The purpose of the first pinhole is to ensure that the waves coming from the next two pinholes are 'coherent'; that is to say, that they keep in step with each other since they come from the one set of spherical waves from the first pinhole.

This effect seemed to clinch the wave nature of light without any doubt. The spacing of the fringes depends on the distance apart of the two pinholes; if they are further apart the waves cross at a steeper angle and the fringes are closer. The effect can only occur if the same original wave goes through both holes. It had been previously widely held that light consisted of particles, an idea supported by the authority of the great Newton, but interference could not be explained by a particle theory. It was agreed that a particle must go through either one hole or the other; if it goes through one how can it 'know' where the other hole is, and so 'know' that it must hit the screen at a bright fringe and not at a dark one?

The attraction of the particle theory of light had been that it accounted so simply for the travelling of light in straight lines, whereas one

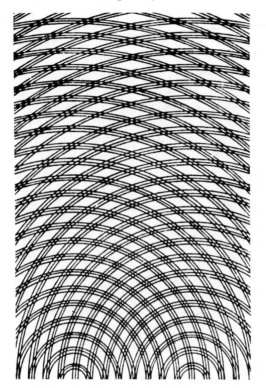

FIG. 3. Young's drawing to illustrate the interference of waves from two sources.

would expect waves to bend round corners. Young himself was puzzled by this problem and could not see the answer. The whole matter was put straight by the elegant work of Fresnel, who showed that the reason why light casts such sharp shadows is that the wavelength of light is so short compared with the dimension of the object casting the shadow. Even so, light from a point source does *not* throw shadows which are absolutely sharp. The edges of the shadows show 'diffraction', a system of fringes created by interference of the light waves which have passed round the edge of the obstacle. Fresnel gave a quantitative explanation of the form of the fringes, and the wave nature of light received further confirmation.

In the 1830's Faraday established the laws of electromagnetic induction, which determine how electric fields and magnetic fields interact. He had the intuition to realize that these laws implied the possibility of 'electromagnetic waves' which could propagate an electric disturbance through space. Faraday was no mathematician, and it was left to Clerk Maxwell to put Faraday's idea into mathematical form. He showed that the velocity of such waves is equal to the velocity of light, so establishing the electromagnetic nature of light waves.

The electric and magnetic fields in the waves are perpendicular to the direction in which they are travelling and therefore the waves can be polarized. Devices can be used which pass light with its electric vector in one direction, while cutting out the electric vector in a direction perpendicular to the first. A familiar example is the polaroid screen used in spectacles which reduce glare. A substance is used whose molecules absorb light vibrating in one direction, while allowing the perpendicular vibration to pass, and a technical device is employed to align the molecules in parallel array. Light reflected from a water surface at about 45° is polarized. If one looks through a polaroid screen at the surface of a pond or stream, in one orientation the glare of reflected light is so great that one can hardly see below the surface, whereas if the polaroid is turned through a right angle the glare disappears and one sees the bottom distinctly.

To sum up, the body of evidence about the nature of light so impressively supported the wave theory, that this seemed to be one of the more firmly established of scientific postulates.

3. The Nature of X-rays

It is now accepted that X-rays are a form of electromagnetic radiation, a part of the great range which extends from the waves used for radio whose length is measured in metres to the waves a million million times shorter, which come from radioactive bodies or reach us from space as cosmic rays. Before 1912, however, when Laue and his colleagues in Germany discovered the diffraction of X-rays by crystals, the nature of X-rays was still a matter of controversy. It is interesting to follow this story, because it sheds so much light on a vital stage in the development of physical ideas and is an important part of the history of physics.

In 1898, three years after Röntgen had discovered the new and mysterious form of radiation, which is called after him, it was suggested by G. G. Stokes that the X-rays are formless pulses of electromagnetic radiation caused by the electrons in the X-ray tube hitting the anticathode. J. J. Thomson later elaborated this into a theory which supposed there were kinks in the tubes of force attached to an electron. When it was suddenly stopped in the anticathode these kinks ran along a line of force rather like the dislocation running along the lash of a whip which is being cracked.

The most active protagonist of the electromagnetic nature of X-rays was C. G. Barkla, who performed experiments in 1905 on the scattering of X-rays which seemed to show clearly that they behaved like light. When a beam of light falls upon a fine mist or a suspension of fine particles in a liquid, the scattered light shows polarization effects (Fig. 4).

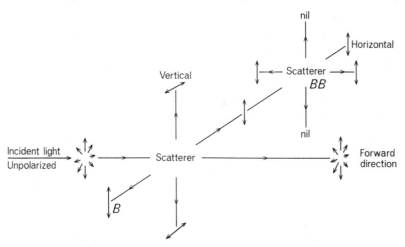

Fig. 4. Diagram showing the polarization of light scattered at right angles to the incident beam. For full explanation see text.

The electric vector in the incident unpolarized beam may be in any direction perpendicular to the beam, and so the light scattered in a forward or backward direction has also vectors in all directions and is unpolarized. In the direction *BB* at right angles to the beam, however, only the vertical component of the electric vector can be propagated and so the light is plane-polarized. The horizontal components of the electric vector in the incident beam are seen 'end on' as it were at *B* and are not transmitted in that direction. This effect is strikingly shown if we look at the light scattered by the sky through a sheet of polaroid which only allows one direction of the electric vector to pass. The light from points near the sun is unpolarized, but in a direction at right angles to the sun the sky alternates between light and dark as the polaroid is turned round.

A consequence of this effect is that twice as much light is scattered backwards or forwards as sideways, and Barkla found that the scattering of X-rays was indeed weaker in the sideways direction. He clinched it by a double-scattering experiment. If the light at BB is scattered again it will be equally strong in all horizontal directions, but zero vertically. From the success of these experiments, Barkla concluded that there was unambiguous proof of the polarization of X-rays.

Two years later he performed another experiment which seemed to receive a natural explanation in terms of waves—he discovered the 'characteristic X-rays', a discovery which won him the Nobel Prize. At that time the only way of assessing the quality of X-rays was by their absorption in matter. Rays which were highly penetrating were called 'hard', those which were heavily absorbed were called 'soft'. A heterogeneous beam composed of hard and soft rays became harder after passing through an absorber, because the softer rays were filtered out. On the other hand if a beam did not alter in character, but merely became weaker, as it traversed absorbing screens it could be assumed that it was 'homogeneous', or all of one quality. Barkla discovered that when X-rays fell upon a body, a homogeneous radiation characteristic of the body came from it, in addition to the scattered incident radiation. The higher the atomic weight of the body the harder the characteristic radiation it produced. (Actually he found two types of such radiation for each element, the harder K radiation and a softer L radiation.) He regarded this phenomenon as equivalent to the excitation of a spectrum, 'a disturbance of the atom, which quickly recovers its normal configuration as it emits a characteristic X-ray,' is how he put it.

In the face of this very strong evidence of the electromagnetic nature of X-rays, which was generally accepted in the scientific world as clinching the matter, my father W. H. Bragg in 1907 proposed the theory that γ-rays, and by implication X-rays also, were material particles. It is interesting to trace the reasons which emboldened him to propose it—they were actually very cogent reasons.

Whereas Barkla had approached the problem from the 'light' end, as it were, and noted the similarities between X-rays and visible light, W. H. Bragg approached by way of his studies on α, β and γ rays from radioactive bodies.

The α-rays are a form of radiation which is very effective in ionizing gases they traverse, but which have very little penetrating power. They are stopped, for instance, by a few centimetres of air. The β-rays are far more penetrating, but ionize less. The researches of Rutherford and others had shown that α-rays are nuclei of helium atoms with a positive charge, and the β-rays are streams of electrons like cathode rays. The γ-rays are the most penetrating, and are like very hard X-rays.

Following his researches on the α-rays, my father made experiments with the γ-rays and the 'secondary β-rays' they produce when they fall upon matter. In support of his theory he listed certain properties of the γ-rays which he had deduced (quite correctly as it later turned out) from his experiments on γ-ray scattering, absorption and β- production. They can be briefly summarized as follows:

(a) When γ-rays are scattered, the scattering is far greater in the forward direction than in the backward direction, and the harder the rays the more marked is the effect. This is in flat contradiction to the scattering of electromagnetic waves as shown in Fig. 4 where the forward and backward scatterings ought to be equal, but it is to be expected if the γ-rays are corpuscular.

(b) The secondary electrons (β-rays) produced by the beam of γ-rays are shot mainly in the forward direction. One would not expect this as the result of a wave's electric field which is perpendicular to the beam.

(c) The energy of the β-rays is characteristic of the hardness of the γ-rays not of the intensity of the beam.

(d) Similarly when X-rays (which are obviously analogous to γ-rays) ionize a gas, the ionization is a secondary effect caused by electrons shot out of the atoms of the gas, and not primarily produced by the X-rays. The energy of these electrons depends only on the nature of the X-rays, being greater for the harder rays. He deduced this from indirect experiments on X-ray ionization. It was later completely confirmed by C. T. R. Wilson's photographs of X-rays travelling through the cloud chamber.

These last features seemed to rule out the wave nature of the rays completely. As my father put it, if one supposed the rays to be waves, it was as if a plank were dropped into a sea from a height of 100 feet, and ripples spread out which had no effect anywhere except that at some point, which might be near or far, a plank was jerked out of a wooden ship and rose exactly 100 feet into the air. It seemed an inescapable conclusion that one γ-ray or one X-ray transmitted its whole energy to one particular electron and this implied that it was a projectile scoring a direct hit on the electron. So my father deduced that γ-rays and X-rays were material particles, and ascribed their high penetrating power and their not being deflected in a magnetic field to their being neutral particles with equal positive and negative components.

One can see now why Barkla was so impressed by the wave-like behaviour of X-rays, whereas my father was so impressed by their particle-like properties. Many years later, in 1922, A. Compton in America showed that X-rays are| scattered by matter in two ways. A part of

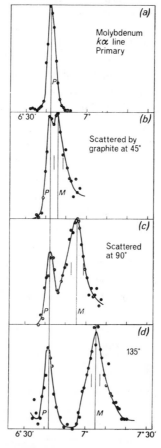

FIG. 5. Analysis by a spectrometer of the X-rays from a molybdenum target scattered by graphite through different angles. The peak on the left corresponds to X-rays of unaltered wavelength while that on the right corresponds to X-rays whose wavelength increases with the angle of the scattering by the graphite according to the Compton shift.

the radiation is scattered without change of wavelength. It is this kind of scattering which produces the interference effects which are the basis of X-ray analysis. The scattered waves are 'coherent' like the waves coming from Young's pinholes. The waves in fact behave just like light waves, following the same laws of scattering and showing interference and polarization; this may be called 'Thomson scattering'. Another part of the radiation is changed to a longer wavelength and the change increases with the angle of 'Compton scattering'—Fig. 5 shows the analysis by a spectrometer of the X-rays from a molybdenum target, scattered by graphite through different angles. The peak on the left remains unaltered in wavelength, while that on the right has the Compton shift. This radiation is not coherent and does not show interference effects.

Compton accounted quantitatively for the shift by treating the radiation as particles which underwent collisions with the electrons and were deflected. The X-ray 'photon' has a momentum $h\nu_0/c$, ν_0 being its frequency and c the velocity of light. It is deflected by a collision with an electron to one side, while the electron recoils to the other side. It

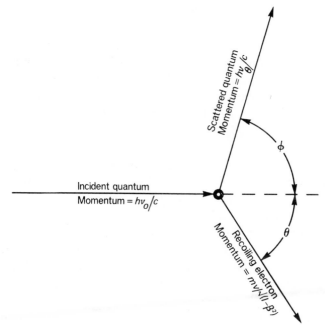

FIG. 6. Compton scattering of X-rays.

loses some of its momentum and energy to the electron, and so its frequency v_0 is decreased to v. This lowering of frequency agrees quantitatively with the longer wavelength shown in Fig. 6. The electrons get a 'knock on' with a forward component, they cannot be thrown backwards.

Actually C. T. R. Wilson had observed these knocked-on electrons arising from the Compton scattering in his cloud chamber. They make short tracks, quite distinct from the much longer tracks of the electrons which have received a quantum hv of energy from the rays, but he had not understood their nature. I remember that when he showed them to me he described them as 'little fish' which seemed to be swimming in the direction of the beam.

Now the Compton effect is more important the harder the rays, and it is far more marked in the case of γ-rays. The γ-rays are predominantly scattered forwards, they become softer, and the secondary β-rays arising from the Compton collisions are shot forwards with a high energy. Barkla, working with soft X-rays, had remarked the analogies with light waves, whereas W. H. Bragg, working with the very hard γ-rays, could not escape the conclusion that they were particles.

A deeper understanding has shown that both sides were right. It is now accepted that both radiation and matter have particle-like and wave-like properties. Nothing could seem to be more definitely a particle than an electron. It has a charge, it is deflected in an electric or magnetic field, and it leaves a narrow trail in a Wilson cloud chamber. Yet a beam of electrons falling on a crystal is diffracted, in a way which can only be explained as being similar to the diffraction of light by a grating. Neutrons, which have the mass of a hydrogen nucleus, are similarly diffracted by crystals.

The position may be summed up as follows. All our records of what *has* happened are records of the behaviour of particles. An electron leaves a trail in a cloud chamber. An α-particle hits a phosphorescent screen and produces a point of light. A quantum of electromagnetic radiation hits one particular electron and gives all its energy to it. A light quantum hits one particular crystal of silver salt in a photographic plate and this turns black on development, all the rest being unaffected. Our record is a history of the behaviour of individual particles at definite points.

On the other hand, if we set up some experiment and wish to predict the results, we have to think of both matter and radiation as waves.

We picture these waves being diffracted or scattered, calculate where they will be strong or weak, and their strength is a measure of the relative probability of the particles turning up at various points as the result of our experiment. We can never predict the result of an experiment precisely, we can only say what is more likely and what is less likely to happen. To say that we must consider radiation and matter to be waves is too narrow a statement. What we are calculating is probabilities, and it so happens that the wave is a convenient way of treating probabilities mathematically. To ask 'are they really waves?' is to raise rather a deeper philosophical question.

So the dividing line between the wave or particle nature of matter and radiation is the moment 'Now'. As this moment steadily advances through time, it coagulates a wavy future into a particle past.

If only it had been realized at the time, the similarity between light and X-rays had been clearly shown by Einstein's explanation in 1905 of the photoelectric effect. He showed that light of frequency v hands over energy to matter in quanta hv, where h is Planck's constant. If light falls on the surface of a metal, the electrons are given an energy $E(= hv)$ and if this is greater than a critical energy E characteristic of the metal they escape and the body can lose a negative electrical charge. It was correct to deduce that X-rays behaved like particles; what was not realized was that this had not differentiated them from light waves because these latter behave in exactly the same way. The significance of Einstein's theory had however not been generally realized, and the controversy was still raging when in 1912 von Laue in Germany made the great discovery which entirely altered the situation.

CHAPTER 2

THE START OF X-RAY ANALYSIS

1. The Discovery of X-ray Diffraction

In 1912, P. P. Ewald was preparing his doctor's dissertation in Munich under the direction of the famous theoretical physicist A. Sommerfeld. He was analysing mathematically the passage of light waves through a crystalline arrangement of scattering atoms arranged in a pattern, and he consulted M. v. Laue, at that time a *Privat-Dozent* in Munich University, about his treatment of the phenomenon. When discussing it, Laue was led to ask Ewald what would happen if the waves were shorter than the interatomic distances in the crystal, not much longer as in the case of light waves. Ewald said that his formula would cover such a case as it had been deduced without any approximations, and gave Laue a copy of the formula. He found that Laue was listening in a 'slightly distracted way' and did not pursue the discussion, and the next he heard about the matter was the news that X-ray diffraction had been discovered. Laue realized that X-rays might satisfy this condition of wavelength smaller than the atomic spacing, and at an informal discussion after a colloquium meeting, W. Friedrich, who was Sommerfeld's research assistant, offered to try the experiment. It is related that Sommerfeld was dubious whether the attempt was worth making, but it came off. The first account of X-ray diffraction was published in the *Proceedings of the Royal Bavarian Academy of Science* in June 1912.

In his paper, Laue started by referring to Barkla's experiments on the scattering of X-rays. Barkla had shown that whereas part of the energy of the incident radiation went into producing the K and L radiations characteristic of the scatterer, the other part was scattered without change of wavelength like light. Therefore, Laue argued, when X-rays pass through a crystal, the atoms would be sources of secondary waves, like the lines in an optical grating, though the diffraction effects would be more complicated because the pattern of atoms is three dimensional.

An estimate of the 'constant' of the crystal grating, or distance at which the pattern repeats, could be got from the molecular weight of the compound, its density, and the numbers of molecules in a gram-molecule. The spacing is of the order 10^{-8} cm, whereas some rather indecisive diffraction experiments of Walter and Pohl, and the theoretical estimates by Sommerfeld and Koch, appeared to indicate X-ray wavelengths of the order of 10^{-9} cm. The conditions for diffraction might therefore be satisfied. Laue says in his paper 'At my instigation Herren Friedrich and Knipping (a young student who assisted Friedrich) have tried out my ideas experimentally. They will therefore give an account of their experiments and their results in the second half of this paper.'

The experimental arrangement adopted by Friedrich and Knipping is shown in Fig. 1. A beam from the X-ray tube passed through a shielding screen and then into a lead box. The last of the windows $B_1B_2B_3B_4$

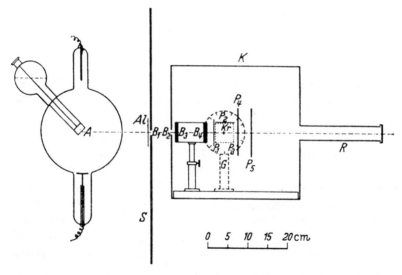

FIG. 1. The Friedrich and Knipping experiment. For details see text.

limited it to a pencil about 1 mm wide which fell on the crystal *Kr*. Photographic plates $P_1P_2P_3P_4P_5$ were distributed around the crystal to catch any diffracted rays.

They tried the experiment first with a crystal of copper sulphate. They had an idea that the characteristic 'fluorescent' radiation from the crystal might be important, and Barkla had shown that atoms of atomic weights in the copper regions were especially effective in producing characteristic radiation. Actually, of course, the fluorescent radiation plays no part in diffraction.

The pioneer photograph of X-ray diffraction is shown in Fig. 2(*a*). It was obtained on a plate such as P_4 in Fig. 1 on the far side of the crystal from the X-ray tube. As a check, the crystal was ground up and placed in a small paper container; the pattern of spots disappeared (Fig. 2(*b*)). When the plate was placed nearer (Fig. 2(*c*)) or further away

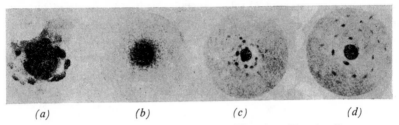

| (a) | (b) | (c) | (d) |

FIG. 2. The pioneer photographs of X-ray diffraction. For details see text.

(Fig. 2(*d*)) the pattern shrank or expanded. The size of the spots did not vary with distance, showing that they were made by parallel beams. If the crystal was tilted, the spots shifted their positions and altered in intensity. In fact, they behaved just as one would expect from the theory of diffraction.

It is interesting to speculate why the effect had never been noticed before in the seventeen years which had elapsed since Röntgen's discovery. Countless experiments on X-rays had been performed. The answer probably lies in the very long exposures which were necessary even with the most powerful water-cooled tubes available in those days, through which a current of ten milliamperes could be passed. Exposures of up to twenty hours were necessary, with frequent halts to let the tube cool. It is very improbable that any experimenter would have gone to such lengths unless he had good reason to hope that his experiments might lead to some very exciting new result.

Friedrich and Knipping then substituted for the crystal of copper sulphate, which had a very low symmetry, one of a highly symmetrical form. A cubic crystal of zincblende, ZnS, was orientated so that X-rays fell normally on a cube face. The result is shown in Fig. 3. The pattern of spots has a complete four-fold symmetry, reflecting the symmetry of the atomic pattern in the crystal. It was clear that the crystal pattern must be the cause of the observed effect.

Friedrich in later years gave an account of this historical discovery which is so interesting that I have quoted it in full below:

'My experience of the intensity of secondary rays told me that really long exposure times were necessary for one to expect a result. Otherwise the phenomenon would have been found long before since in looking for double refraction and polarization crystals had often been irradiated with X-rays. Fortunately a large induction coil and also a powerful

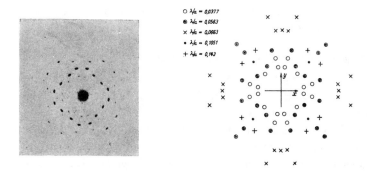

Fig. 3. Friedrich and Knipping's diffraction photograph of zinc sulphide with von Laue's interpretation.

Gundelach tube was available at the Institute thanks to the co-operation of Sommerfeld. It was harder to choose a suitable crystal. We believed at first the phenomenon was a result of a characteristic secondary radiation of the crystal. Consequently the first experiments were carried out in an unprofitable way. The photographic plates set parallel to the primary rays showed only a little characteristic blackening. Although in principle the theory of the interference effects was already available, it had not been exactly worked out by Laue; above all the nature of the effect was not yet known. Only when we placed a plate behind the crystal did we obtain the well known photograph of interference effects, after many hours exposure, which is shown in Fig. 2. It was an unforgettable experience when late in the evening all alone in my laboratory in the Institute, I stood before the developing dish and saw the traces of the diffracted rays appear on the plate. Next day my first action was to go to Knipping and show him the plate. We hurried to Laue and to my Chief, where naturally there was the liveliest discussion of the picture. Thanks to the great interest and co-operation of Sommerfeld, it was possible to finish the investigation further with the extensive means of the Institute. In great spirits I abandoned my work on "Bremsstrahlen' [the task he had been set by Sommerfeld]. Also Röntgen and Groth, who had simultaneously seen the results, did not hesitate to support us. So we built a better experimental set-up and soon the irradiation of regular crystals in the crystallographic direction showed us the full beauty of the interference phenomenon in the well-known diagrams. Meanwhile Laue had developed further the theory of the effect and on 8th June 1912, Sommerfeld was able to submit to the Munich Academy our well-known work in interference phenomena, by which the wave nature of X-rays was decisively proved.'

2. Laue's Analysis of the Diffraction Pattern

When light falls normally on a diffraction grating as in Fig. 4, secondary wavelets are scattered from each line of the grating. These wavelets not only recombine into a transmitted wave travelling in the same direction as the incident light, but also combine into a series of waves deflected to each side. Figure 4 shows the zero order, first order, and second order spectra. If the spacing of the grating is a, and the wavelength of the light is λ, the nth order spectrum comes off at an angle θ given by

$$n\lambda = a \sin \theta.$$

This formula expresses the condition that the path difference for waves from successive lines is n wavelengths, and therefore the wavelets reinforce.

In three dimensions the conditions are of course more complicated. The pattern repeats in three directions and in order that a diffracted beam

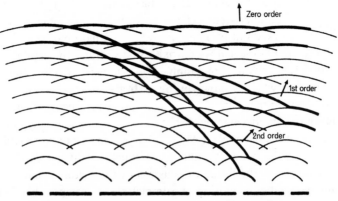

FIG. 4. Formation of spectra by a line grating.

may build up, the path difference must be a whole number of wavelengths for each of these directions. Just as *n* denotes the order of the spectrum for a one-dimensional grating, three integers h_1, h_2, h_3 denote the order for a three-dimensional grating.

Laue took the simple case of diffraction by a cubical pattern when the incident rays are parallel to the z edge of the cube, as in the experiment on zincblende. The conditions for diffraction are shown in Fig. 5.

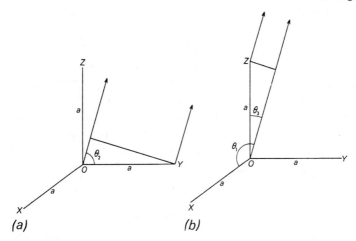

Fig. 5. Laue theory of diffraction by a cubical pattern when incident rays are parallel to an edge of the cube. For details see text.

The pattern repeats along the axes of reference *OX*, *OY*, *OZ* at intervals of *a*. The diffracted rays are in the direction shown by the arrow, which makes angles θ_1, θ_2, θ_3, with the axes. The path differences between rays diffracted by adjacent lattice points along the three axes (Figs. 5(a) and 5(b)) are:

$$a \cos \theta_1 \text{ for } O \text{ and } X$$
$$a \cos \theta_2 \text{ for } O \text{ and } Y$$
$$a(1 - \cos \theta_3) \text{ for } O \text{ and } Z.$$

Hence the Laue conditions

$$\alpha = h_1\lambda/a \qquad \beta = h_2\lambda/a \qquad 1 - \gamma = h_3\lambda/a$$

where the direction cosines α, β, γ are written for $\cos \theta_1$, $\cos \theta_2$, $\cos \theta_3$.

Laue tested the application of this formula to the zincblende picture in a paper which followed soon after the publication of the first results.

In the first place, the quantities α, β, $(1 - \gamma)$ should be in the ratio of whole numbers for each spot in the picture, because they are proportional to the integers h_1, h_2, h_3. He checked that this condition was satisfied, generally by a triplet of simple numbers.

The next test was to see what values of λ/a accounted for the spots. He found that there was a reasonable agreement if he supposed there were in the X-rays five wavelengths, like five lines in a spectrum, with values (Fig. 3)

$$\lambda/a = 0.0377, 0.0563, 0.0663, 0.1051, 0.143$$

He expressed these in terms of λ/a, because it is not possible to calculate a unless the number of molecules associated with each point of the grating is known, and this was still uncertain.

This explanation was not entirely satisfactory because spots which could have been made by these wavelengths were absent from the photograph. Laue's theoretical treatment left no doubt, however, that he was correct in his main conclusion that the spots were produced by diffraction.

3. A Reinterpretation of Laue's Photographs

At the time Laue published his results, I was a research student at Cambridge in the Cavendish Laboratory directed by J. J. Thomson. I was naturally very interested in Laue's work, because it so vitally affected my father's theory that X-rays were particles. My father and I discussed the effects together in the summer vacation of 1912, and towards its end I set up an unsuccessful experiment in his laboratory in Leeds to test whether the spots were not due to waves but due to X-ray particles being shot down avenues between the atoms in the crystal structure. I made a small window at one end of a lead-lined box, and at the other end I placed a photographic plate wrapped in black paper. The box was so pivoted on gimbals that it could rotate about vertical and horizontal axes, the hole remaining in the same position. The hole was covered with a section of a crystal. An X-ray tube was placed in front of the hole, and I laboriously by hand adjusted the box in all positions in turn inside a solid angle, thinking that if the rays shot down avenues these would show up on the photographic plate, since the crystal and plate remained fixed relative to each other. I got no positive results and I was unaware at the time that J. Stark had put forward a similar explanation of the origin of Laue's pattern.

When I returned to Cambridge I studied Laue's photographs further, and it was then that I had the 'brain wave' which led to my maiden effort in research, and which advanced X-ray analysis to its next stage.

My generation of students had been inspired by the lectures on Physical Optics given by C. T. R. Wilson in the Cavendish Laboratory. In particular he had given us a lecture on white light in which he showed that when light falls on a diffraction grating we can either regard it as composed of light of all colours, which are sorted out by the grating into a spectrum, or we can regard it as a series of irregular pulses from which the grating manufactures the trains of waves which form the spectrum.

In Fig. 4 a monochromatic train of wavelength λ falls normally on a grating and the wavelets coming from the lines build up a zero order spectrum, a first order spectrum, a second order spectrum and so forth as shown in the figure. If white light, with a continuous range of wavelengths, falls on the grating each wavelength will be diffracted through a corresponding angle θ given by $\lambda = a \sin \theta$, and the whole will be spread out into a spectrum from blue at small angles to red at large angles. In Fig. 6 a formless electromagnetic pulse is pictured as falling on the

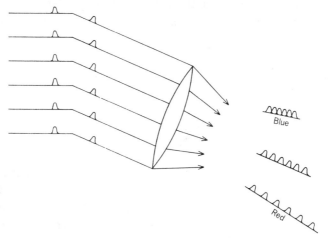

FIG. 6. Diffraction by a grating of a formless electromagnetic pulse.

grating. Each of the N lines of the grating will transmit this pulse, and the telescope will receive N samples of the pulse at intervals of $a \cdot \sin \theta$ because of the differences in the lengths of the path the pulses have to follow. A harmonic analysis separates this train of pulses into light of a fundamental wavelength $a \cdot \sin \theta$, and upper harmonics of wavelength

($a\cdot\sin\,\theta$)/2, ($a\cdot\sin\,\theta$)/3 etc. The periodic quality which causes the light to be of one colour is created by the grating; one need not suppose it to be present in the original light.

The same reasoning holds for a prism, though the analysis is not quite so direct. In fact, when Newton made his famous experiment of admitting sunlight through a slit in his window and analysing it into colours by passing it through his prism, we might equally well say that it was the prism which created the colours.

One can carry the comparison further. A broad pulse of light is equivalent to a range of wavelengths mainly in the long region, whereas a narrow pulse represents a range in the short region. In Fig. 6 it is clear that whereas at large angles the broad pulses will be well separated and so give a strong wave, at small angles they will overlap and the net result will be small. The spectrum will be strong at the red end, weak at the blue end. On the other hand, narrow pulses give a strong effect in the blue region. The alternative ways of regarding the phenomenon are merely two ways of looking at the same thing.

I was led to think whether Laue's results might be due, not to a few definite wavelengths in the incident X-rays as he supposed, but to the action of the crystal grating on the formless pulses of radiation

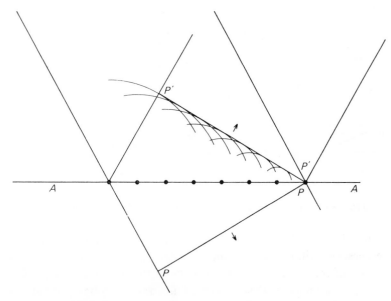

FIG. 7. The reflection of a wavefront by points lying on a plane.

which Stokes had supposed to constitute X-rays. I realized that such pulses would give diffracted spots, because they must be reflected by the planes of the crystal lattice in definite directions. The points of the lattice can be regarded as arranged in sheets in a number of different ways. When a wave first falls on a sheet the wavelets scattered by the points build up a reflected wave as in the famous Huygens construction (Fig. 7). When I applied this test to Laue pictures it was at once clear that all the spots were indeed in positions explained by reflection in the crystal planes. As a check I set up an experiment in which a fine beam of X-rays fell upon a sheet of mica. Mica cleaves so readily that one would expect the sheets of atoms parallel to the cleavage to be well marked. I found that for any angle of incidence of the rays, the mica always gave a reflected beam as if it were a mirror reflecting the radiation. I vividly remember taking my plate, still wet from the fixing dish, down to J. J. Thomson's room and showing it to him. It was very gratifying to see my professor's great excitement.

It was now possible to trace a complete analogy between the diffraction of X-rays by the crystal, and C. T. R. Wilson's treatment of the effect of a grating on pulses. The points of the crystal lattice can be arranged in series of parallel planes, each of which reflects a fraction of a wavefront.

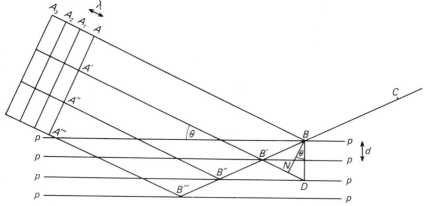

FIG. 8. The reflection of a wave train by successive lattice planes.

When therefore a pulse traverses the crystal, a train of pulses is reflected as in Fig. 8. The crystal is turning the pulse into trains of monochromatic waves, like the action of the grating in Fig. 6. Alternatively, we may regard the pulse as a range of X-ray wavelengths, and the reflecting planes as sorting out one wavelength and its harmonics for reflection.

The path difference between the waves of the reflected train is $2d \sin \theta$, when θ is the glancing angle at which the radiation falls on the planes, and d is their spacing. Hence the wavelengths of the different orders are given by

$$n\lambda = 2d \sin \theta$$

where n is an integer. This relation is known as 'Bragg's law', and I have always felt the association of my name with it to be an easily earned honour, because it is merely the familiar optical relation giving the colours reflected by thin films, in another guise.

The next test to make was to see whether the pulse idea explained why some reflections appeared in Laue's zincblende pattern (Fig. 3) and others did not, and here also the analogy with C. T. R. Wilson's treatment can be used. If one thinks of the pulse as a continuous range of wavelengths, which is strong in the centre of the range and falls off to either side, then all planes should give a strong reflection if the wavelength they diffract falls in the strong part of the range, and vice versa. The points of the lattice were assumed to be at the corners of cubes with a spacing a, and the spacings of the reflecting planes were calculated in terms of a. The law for reflection gave the value of λ/a for each spot, and one could check whether their values fall within a certain range of 'white' radiation.

To my great disappointment the first test did not work, in that spots were absent which should be there and vice versa, but I found the reason which is illustrated in Fig. 9. There are three point groups which have

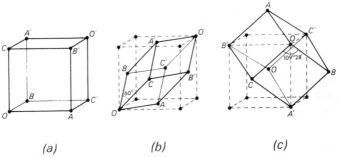

(a)   (b)   (c)

FIG. 9. The three cubic point groups.

cubic symmetry. The simplest is (a) which has a point at each corner of the cube. Fig. 9(b) has additional points at the centres of the faces and Fig. 9(c) at cube centres. In all three the points are equivalent, or can be seen by the primitive cells outlined in the figure with a point at each corner;

they are shown as face-centred and body-centred so as to display the cubic symmetry.

For instance, if one takes an origin at the middle of the cube in Fig. 9(c) it becomes a corner and the former corners become centres.

The relative spacings of the planes are different for these three point groups. A set of planes is identified by three numbers which are the inverse of the lengths they intercept on the axes. For instance, in the simple cubic lattice, the set (100) describes planes which intercept a on the x axis, and are parallel to (and so make an infinite intercept on) the y and z axes, and similarly for (010) and (001). The planes (110) make equal intercepts a on x and y, and are parallel to z; for (111) the intercepts are a on all three axes.

In the case of the simple cube (Fig. 9(a)) the spacings of these three types of plane are OC; the perpendicular from O on AB; and the perpendicular from O on ABC, which are equal to a, $a/\sqrt{2}$ and $a/\sqrt{3}$. When additional points are introduced at the face centres, the planes of the first two types are twice as close, while the new points still lie on the (111) planes so their spacing is unaltered. The intercepts are $a/2$, $a/2\sqrt{2}$, $a/\sqrt{3}$. Similarly in Fig. 9(c) they are $a/2$, $a/\sqrt{2}$, $a/2\sqrt{3}$. So the order of spacings is

Simple Cubic	(100), (110), (111).
Face-centred Cubic	(111), (200), (220).
Body-centred Cubic	(110), (200), (222).

I found that, although the range of wavelengths represented by the spots did not make sense if one assumed ZnS to be based on a simple cubic lattice everything fell into place if one assumed the basic lattice to be face-centred cubic. Every case where a reflection came into a certain range of λ/a values was represented by a spot in the photograph with the strongest in the middle of the range and a fading away on either side. No spots which should have been there were missing. Further, Laue had taken photographs with the crystal slightly tilted from the symmetrical position. The reflections moved and the wavelengths correspondingly changed. I was able to show that spots got stronger if they moved from the edge of the spectral range to the middle, and weaker if they moved the other way. These results showed, not only that Laue's pictures were made by a continuous range of X-ray wavelengths, a kind of 'white' radiation, but also that X-ray diffraction *could be used to get information about the nature of the crystal pattern.*

It is interesting to reflect now how it came about that this simpler way of explaining his results did not occur to Laue, who had so penetrating an insight into diffraction phenomena. It may be because the three-dimensional diffraction has an essential quality quite unlike one-dimensional or two-dimensional diffraction. When a continuous range of wavelengths falls on one- or two-dimensional gratings, the result is a continuous spectrum, and so that the occurrence of discrete spots on Laue's photographs may have suggested there must be discrete wavelengths in the incident radiation. To me, the moment of revelation came with the idea of 'reflection', because pulses are regularly reflected, independently of any wavelength condition—and so the discrete spots are at once explained.

4. The Equivalence of the Laue and Reflection Conditions

According to the Laue conditions the difference in path length for rays scattered at O and at A in Fig. 10 must be $h\lambda$, and similarly $k\lambda$ for O and B, and $l\lambda$ for O and C where h, k, l are integers. The Laue conditions for the general case are therefore

$$h\lambda = a(\alpha - \alpha_0)$$
$$k\lambda = b(\beta - \beta_0)$$
$$l\lambda = c(\gamma - \gamma_0)$$

where α_0, β_0, γ_0 are the cosines of the angles between the incident ray and the axes *abc*, and α, β, γ the corresponding cosines for the diffracted ray. Suppose now that in Fig. 10 the *a* axis is divided into h parts, and that

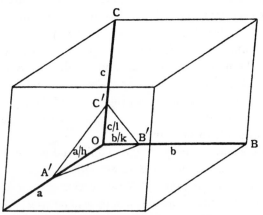

FIG. 10. Equivalence of 'Laue' and 'reflection' conditions.

OA′ = a/h and similarly OB′ = b/k, OC′ = c/l, the rays scattered by A′B′C′ will then each differ in path by one wavelength from those scattered at O. They will thus be in phase with each other, and this is the condition for reflection of the incident beam on the plane A′B′C′. (The indices *hkl* are now more generally employed than Laue's integers h_1, h_2 h_3.) The construction for drawing planes such as A′B′C′ is at the same time the construction for drawing the net planes on which the points of the lattice lie. For instance the point A′ has been drawn in the figure half-way along the axis *a*, so the next plane will pass through the point A′ and similarly for B′ and C′, and this will in turn be true for every point of the lattice.

Next, the condition for one wavelength path difference between O and A′B′C′ implies one wavelength path difference between successive parallel planes, so the Bragg condition $\lambda = 2d \sin \theta$ is satisfied. The Laue condition and the reflection condition are equivalent.

The external faces of a crystal are parallel to the net planes, and similar indices called Millerian indices are used to describe the crystal faces. There is an important point to note in this connection. The Millerian indices (*hkl*) give the orientation of a crystal face and so can be the simplest which describe the fractions into which the crystal axes are divided (Fig. 10); they contain no common factor. The order (*hkl*) has no such restriction. There may be orders (*hkl*), (2*h*, 2*k*, 2*l*) (3*h*, 3*k*, 3*l*) and so forth, which represent the first, second and third order Bragg reflections from the (*hkl*) planes.

Although the Bragg law for reflection is only a restatement of the Laue condition, such advantage as it possessed arose from the ease with which it could be understood and its suggestiveness for experiment.

5. The First Complete Analyses: The Alkaline Halides

Professor Pope, who was head of the Cambridge Chemistry Department, was very interested in these indications of the structure of zinc-blende because they seemed to support a theory of crystal structure which he and Barlow had proposed. He encouraged me to make experiments with the crystals of the alkaline halides which he expected would have simpler structures; in fact they proved to be so simple that it was possible to analyse their complete atomic arrangement. The Laue photographs of KCl, KBr, and NaCl are shown diagrammatically in Fig. 11. The size of the spots indicates their relative intensity. The X-rays in each case are parallel to the *Z* axis, and the numbers indicate the indices of the reflecting planes referred to a simple cubic lattice.

The common structure which explains their photographs is shown in Fig. 12. It is based on a series of cubes with an atom at each corner, the

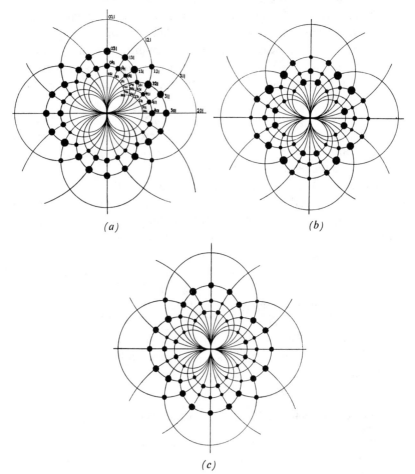

(a)

(b)

(c)

FIG. 11. The Laue diffraction patterns of (a) KCl, (b) KBr and (c) NaCl.

atoms along the cube edges being alternately an alkaline atom and a halogen. The simple X-ray pattern yielded by KCl corresponds to the simplest possible arrangement of scattering points. The atoms of K and Cl are so nearly equal in atomic weight that they are practically equal in scattering power, and hence the structure (Fig. 12) is one of identical points at the corners of cubes. Since the spots in Fig. 11 (*a*) all have $h_3 = 1$, the wavelength at an angle θ_3

$$\lambda = a(1 - \cos \theta_3)$$

and so increases steadily in going out radially from the centre of the photograph. It will be seen that all the spots occur in a definite zone around the centre, strongest in the middle and diminishing on either side, representing a range of wavelengths in the 'white' radiation from the X-ray tube.

The photographs of KBr and NaCl are less simple. The spots with all-odd indices appear to behave in a different way from those with mixed

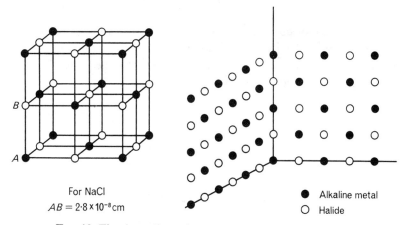

For NaCl
$AB = 2\cdot8 \times 10^{-8}$ cm

● Alkaline metal
○ Halide

FIG. 12. The three-dimensional structure of alkaline halides.

indices. For instance 151 and 351 are quite strong in KBr and NaCl, whereas they are absent in KCl. Also 151 and 131 are strong compared with the intermediate 141. The structure in Fig. 12 explains this difference. Since Br has a higher atomic weight than K, and Cl one higher than Na, they are more efficient scatterers, and in consequence the structure assumes a face-centred character with a cube edge twice as great as that of the simple cube. This makes no difference to the spacings of the sheets of atoms which, in the simple cube, would be labelled (100) and (110) because they contain equal numbers of alkali and halogen atoms. If one traces the planes (111), however, it will be seen that they are alternately packed with alkali and halogen, and this is the case for all sets with odd indices. Since the halogen is heavier *the spacing is doubled*, and these planes can reflect

a radiation of twice the wavelength when compared with the corresponding KCl planes where K and Cl are indistinguishable. This brings new
planes into the range which reflects a strong part of the spectrum, and
hence the corresponding spots such as 131 and 151 can now appear.

It was on this rather indirect and slender evidence that I assigned
the structure of Fig. 12 to the alkaline halides in a paper read to the
Royal Society in June 1913; fortunately further investigation established
its correctness! These were the first crystals to be analysed by X-rays.
As the structure was now established, it was possible to calculate dimensions from the crystal density and the mass of the NaCl molecule. Half a
molecule is associated with each small cube of side $a = $ AB in Fig. 12 so

$$\tfrac{1}{2} \cdot Mm = \varrho a^3$$

where M is the molecular weight, m the mass of the hydrogen atom, and
ϱ is the density of the crystal. This gave a value for a of 2.8×10^{-8} cm as
shown in Fig. 12 and so first established a scale for the measurement of all
X-ray wavelengths and crystal spacings.

CHAPTER 3

THE X-RAY SPECTROMETER

1. The Design of the Instrument

I called my first paper on the interpretation of Laue's results, which was read to the Cambridge Philosophical Society in November 1912, 'The Diffraction of Short Electromagnetic Waves by a Crystal'. I avoided calling them 'X-rays' because I still hoped that my father's theory of their particle nature might be true, and that Laue's effects were due to some kind of waves accompanying the X-rays. It was naturally of prime importance to check whether the reflected rays were actually X-rays, and for this purpose my father designed an instrument to examine their properties such as their absorption and the ionization they caused.

The 'X-ray Spectrometer', as it was termed, played a major role in all the early investigations both of the nature of X-rays and the structure of crystals. It was the forerunner of the complex and powerful instruments which are now used. I appeared as co-author of the paper which was read to the Royal Society in April 1913 because I had established the reflection principle and shown the connection between angle of reflection and wavelength, but I had no hand in the design of the instrument that was constructed in the Leeds workshop by its clever head mechanic, Jenkinson.

The apparatus, the scheme of which is shown in Fig. 1, resembled an optical spectrometer. A slit at O in front of the X-ray tube acted as collimator, the crystal which was mounted on a table that could turn around an axis at P represented the grating, and the ionization chamber which received the reflected rays through a slit at Q, and which was on an arm turning around P, represented the telescope. The settings of crystal and chamber were read on a circular scale around P. The amount of radiation entering Q was measured by applying a potential of about 100 volts to the outer wall of the chamber, and driving the ions to a central insulated wire along its axis. The wire was connected to a Wilson gold-leaf electroscope, which measured the charge it received. In order to

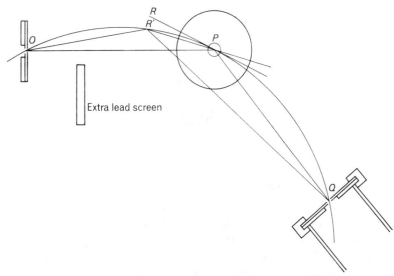

FIG. 1. The design of the X-ray spectrometer.

increase the effect, the chamber was filled with a heavy gas such as sulphur dioxide or methyl iodide. The X-ray tube was enclosed in a lead box to reduce stray radiation.

Considering the primitive nature of the apparatus it gave surprisingly accurate results. A main difficulty was the irregular behaviour of the X-ray tubes available at that time. They generally got hard in use, because the gas in them was driven into the walls of the tube by the discharge, and they had to be softened by judiciously applying a flame to a small palladium tube like an appendix, which when hot allowed a little hydrogen to diffuse into the tube and soften it. The ingenious tilted gold-leaf electroscope devised by Wilson was very temperamental, and only had a linear response over a restricted range. I think that a main reason why the new world opened up by Laue's discovery was explored to such an extent in Great Britain and not in its country of origin was my father's experience and expertise in making accurate ionization measurements. The examination of the effects by ionization rather than by long photographic exposures was more elastic and adaptable; it lent itself to getting quantitative information, and it was easier to analyse results because the positions both of the crystal and the diffracted beam were measured for each reflection. It paid to resist the temptation of the easy photographic recording, and brave the tricky ionization measurements.

A photograph of the original X-ray spectrometer is shown in Fig. 2.

FIG. 2. The original form of the X-ray spectrometer. LLL, lead box. V, Vernier of crystal table. A, B, D, slits. V, Vernier of ionization chamber. C, crystal. K, earthing key. I, ionization chamber. E, electroscope. M, microscope.

2. The Discovery of X-ray Spectra

The first tests on the reflected rays showed that they had the characteristic properties of X-rays, and a review was made of their reflection over a wide range of angles by a number of crystals. One of the first results is shown in Fig. 3. Superimposed upon a general background of

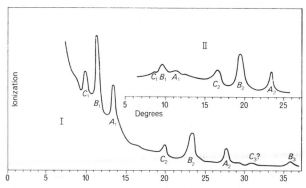

FIG. 3. X-ray spectrometer measurements of X-rays reflected from a sodium chloride crystal. I, from the (100) face; II, from the (111) face.

white radiation, the existence of which had been postulated to explain the Laue photographs, peaks were found which proved that there were definite 'monochromatic' lines in the spectrum of the X-rays. The group of three peaks from the platinum anticathode appeared in every case, though the angles differed for different crystal faces.

Measurements of these spectra provided a far more powerful way of examining crystal structure. For instance, the solution of the sodium chloride structure, so laboriously deduced from the Laue photographs, is now seen at once just from the two curves in Fig. 3. The planes parallel to the (100) face of the crystal (see Ch. 2, Fig. 12) are identical, containing an equal number of sodium and chlorine atoms, and have a spacing $a/2$ where a is the side of the unit cube. These planes give a series of orders $C_1B_1A_1$, $C_2B_2A_2$, C_3B_3—, which diminish regularly in intensity towards higher angles, as shown by I. The planes parallel to (111) contain alternately chlorine and sodium. The spacing from chlorine to chlorine is $a/\sqrt{3}$, hence the first order appears, as shown in curve II, at a lower angle than in I. This first order is weak because there are sodium-containing planes half-way between the chlorine planes and these reflect waves in opposite phase to those reflected from the chlorine planes. The second order is strong because sodium and chlorine now reinforce, being in the same phase. The whole story of the atomic arrangement in Chapter 2, Fig. 12 can be read in these two curves, and it was clear that the spectrometer provided a highly efficient way of analysing crystal structures.

The X-ray spectrometer therefore opened up two lines of investigation, the exploration of the X-ray spectra emitted by different elements, and the analysis of crystal structure. My father was mainly interested in X-rays because he had done so much work in that field, and it fell to me to use the spectrometer for deducing the atomic arrangement in a number of crystals.

Some of the first results obtained by my father with the X-ray spectrometer will now be described. Since that time, far more sophisticated and penetrating methods have been developed, but the principles were established by the first experiments, and their very simplicity is an advantage in understanding these principles.

3. The *K* and *L* Series of Barkla

The body of knowledge about X-rays at the time these investigations started was mainly due to C. G. Barkla. By a series of most ingenious experiments, he had deduced that elements, when stimulated by incident

X-rays, emitted two types of characteristic radiation, which he called the
K and the L types. As was mentioned in chapter 1, the only method of
assessing the quality of radiation which was available to him was by
measuring absorption. A penetrating radiation was called 'hard', one easily absorbed was called 'soft'. A heterogeneous radiation which was a
mixture of hard and soft would become harder when passed through absorbing screens, because the softer part would undergo a greater absorption. If on the other hand a radiation did not alter in quality as it passed
through absorbers, but merely diminished in intensity, it could be assumed to be homogeneous. The absorption of rays in aluminium was a
useful index of quality. Barkla established the following features.

(a) An element, when irradiated, emits a characteristic harder K radia-
     tion, and a softer L radiation.

(b) The hardness of both types of radiation increases with atomic
     weight.

(c) An element can only emit a characteristic radiation when stimulated
     by X-rays which are harder than the characteristic.

(d) In general the absorption of rays increases rapidly with the atomic
     weight of the absorber, as Röntgen had noted in his original paper.
     There is, however, a discontinuity in the absorption. As the hardness
     of the radiation is increased it is absorbed less and less by a given
     element, until its quality reaches the quality of the radiation charac-
     teristic of the element. At that point there is an abrupt rise in the
     absorption, followed by a further steady decline as the radiation
     becomes still harder.

This phenomenon (d) is obviously related to (c). If just softer than
the characteristic, radiation cannot lose energy in stimulating it, but
if just harder its energy can be dissipated in this way and the absorption
goes up.

The advent of the spectrometer made it possible to express these
rules in a way which was more simple and quantitative. Barkla's quality
was defined as wavelength, hard rays being shorter waves, and soft rays
longer waves. Homogeneous X-rays were waves of one wavelength.

X-ray tubes were made with anticathodes of different metals and their
spectra were measured. It was found that the wavelength decreased regularly with increasing atomic weight. The three spectral lines from
platinum, shown in Fig. 3, were identified by their absorption as belong-
ing to Barkla's softer L series as were similar lines given by anticathodes of

osmium, iridium, and tungsten, and these lines were labelled $L\alpha$, $L\beta$, and $L\gamma$. Anticathodes of elements lower in the periodic table such as copper and nickel, or palladium and rhodium, gave two characteristic lines in Barkla's K series, labelled $K\alpha$ and $K\beta$. As an instance the peaks for palladium and rhodium are shown in Fig. 4.

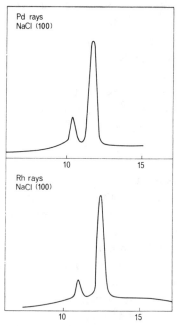

FIG. 4. Characteristic $K\alpha$ and $K\beta$ radiation from palladium and rhodium.

Absorption edges. The abrupt increase in absorption when the wavelength is so short that it can stimulate the characteristic radiation is illustrated by Fig. 5. The upper curve shows the platinum peaks reflected by rock salt, with what one might term their normal relative intensity. The middle curve is for reflection in a crystal of sodium arsenate; the C peak has been heavily absorbed as compared with B and A. The lower curve shows the reflection by zincblende, and here both C and B are heavily absorbed. These changes are explained by the following data.

Wavelengths of Pt peaks. 　$L\alpha$ 　　1.315 Å
　　　　　　　　　　　　$L\beta$ 　　1.114 Å
　　　　　　　　　　　　$L\gamma$ 　　0.955 Å
Absorption edge of arsenic 　　1.042 Å
Absorption edge of zinc 　　　1.280 Å

Lγ can excite the arsenic radiation and so is heavily absorbed. Both *Lγ* and *Lβ* can excite the zinc radiation. *Lα* is too long in wavelength to excite either radiation and so passes with relatively little absorption.

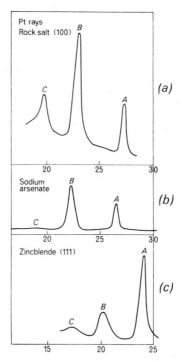

FIG. 5. Variations in reflected X-ray intensities arising from absorption effect. For details see text.

The quantum relationship. Einstein had shown that the photoelectric effect could be explained if it were assumed that light waves falling on a metal surface handed over bundles of energy to the electrons given by the quantum relationship

$$E = h\nu$$

when E is the energy delivered to the electron, ν is the frequency of the light, and h is Planck's constant 6.55×10^{-27} on the c.g.s. scale. Conversely electrons with energy E can produce light of frequency ν according to the same relationship. These are special cases of Planck's general law.

Whiddington had measured the energy of the electrons required to excite Barkla's characteristic K or L radiation for the different elements.

According to his figures the electron-energy required to excite radiation whose absorption coefficient in aluminium corresponded to that of the L radiation of platinum, was 2.30×10^{-8} ergs. The energy corresponding to the $L\gamma$ line of platinum according to the quantum relationship

$$6.55 \times 10^{-27} \cdot 3 \times 10^{10}/0.955 \times 10^{-8} = 2.05 \times 10^{-8} \text{ ergs}$$

which is in good accord with Whiddington's measurement, considering the approximate nature of the data. This agreement was very significant, because it showed for the first time that Einstein's photoelectric equation for visible light extended all the way out to the X-ray region. It was a further proof of the identical nature of light and X-rays.

The Debye effect. Figure 6 shows the effect of temperature on the spectra. These measurements were made with the spectrometer in 1914, and it is remarkable that even at that early stage P. Debye had anticipated that there would be a temperature effect and calculated its magnitude. His

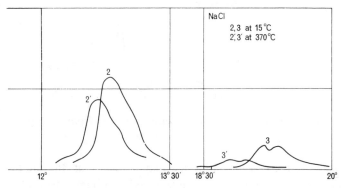

FIG. 6. The effect of temperature on the intensities of the spectra.

formula shows that the intensity of the reflection is reduced by a factor $e^{-B \sin^2 \theta}$ when B is proportional to the mean square of the amplitude of vibration, which increases as the temperature rises. The vibrations make the reflecting planes diffuse, and this reduces the strength of reflection, especially for the higher orders.

The curves show the second and third orders of the rhodium $K\alpha$ line, reflected from a cube face of NaCl at $15°$ and $370°$. It will be seen that as well as a diminution in intensity there is a shift towards smaller angles at the higher temperature owing to the thermal expansion of the crystal. The spectrometer provides a convenient way of measuring amplitudes of atomic vibration and expansion coefficients.

4. The Intensity of Reflection

The paper by my father in the *Philosophical Magazine* for May 1914, which described the measurements on the Debye effect and many other interesting observations on X-ray reflection, contained a contribution which had a very great influence on subsequent developments.

How can the intensity of reflection be defined? In the first crude measurements it was estimated from the relative heights of the peaks when crystal and chamber are turned through the reflecting positions. This is not a sound method, because the peak height depends upon chance characteristics of the crystal conformation. Crystals are not perfect, except when great pains have been taken in growing them. They consist of a mosaic, like a crazy paving, of small blocks of crystal which are

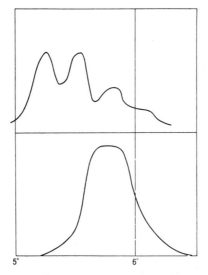

FIG. 7. Reflection profiles from two regions of the same NaCl crystal face.

not precisely parallel. As a crystal is turned through the reflecting position, each block reflects when the angle is right for it, so that the crystal reflects over a range of angles and the maximum peak height depends on how the blocks are arranged. Figure 7 shows the result of measuring the strength of reflection over a range of angles from two regions on the same NaCl face. It is clear that the heights of the maxima are poor guides of intensity.

The uncertainty can be removed by integrating the area under the curves in Fig. 7, or by the equivalent process of turning the crystal at a steady rate and measuring the total ionization in the chamber as it sweeps through the reflecting position. In such a case each element of the mosaic has its opportunity to contribute to the total reflection. It does not matter how large or small the mosaic elements are, or how they are arranged, the total effect must be the same.

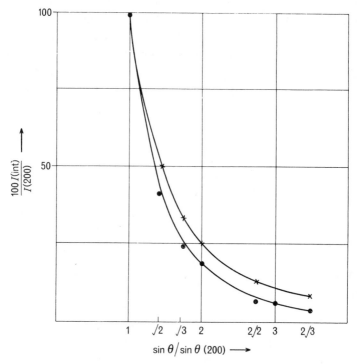

FIG. 8. Relationship between integrated intensities of reflections from rock salt.

It is not necessary to move the ionization chamber during the sweep as is shown by Fig. 1. If the distance from collimator to crystal face, and crystal face to chamber slit, are equal, then to a close approximation the crystal face coincides with the arc of a circle passing through the two slits. The angle subtended by the two slits at any point on the crystal face is closely the same all over the face, so any mosaic element always reflects its rays to the chamber.

Figure 8 shows the result of applying this method of measurement to the reflections from rocksalt. The spots on the lower curve are, in order, (200), (220), (222), (400), (440), (600), (444), the value of (200) being taken to be 100. Since the indices are all even, the sodium and chlorine contributions are in phase.

The measurements proved a very important point. The spots for different faces lie on a smooth curve, showing that all the sets of reflections conform to the same law. Their nearness to the curve shows that the sweep method gives consistent results. Incidentally, the accuracy of intensity measurement shown by their curves is remarkable considering the primitive apparatus used at that time: it could be considered quite good now. The intensity falls off with increasing angle somewhat faster than $1/\sin^2\theta$, the values of which are plotted as crosses in the upper curve.

The method of sweeping the crystal through the reflecting position and integrating the reflected energy can be used to get a true measure of 'Absolute Intensity of Reflection'. If E is the total energy reflected, ω is the angular rate at which the crystal is turned, and I is the energy falling per second on the crystal, then

$$E\omega/I$$

is a dimensionless quantity. It does not depend on the size of the collimating slit or the rate of turning. It is a constant for each type of reflection, and so can be used as an index of intensity for that type.

The sweep method has remained ever since the standard method of making quantitative measurements of X-ray diffraction.

CHAPTER 4

X-RAY SPECTROSCOPY

1. Moseley's Review of X-ray Spectra

The discovery of X-ray spectra was followed up by H. J. G. Moseley at Manchester. Moseley had been working on radioactive substances with the other students in Rutherford's laboratory, but he was deeply interested in Laue's discovery and proposed to C. G. Darwin that they should collaborate in studying X-ray diffraction. Darwin relates that Rutherford tried to discourage them because there was no tradition of X-ray work in the laboratory—a curious parallel to Sommerfeld's lack of enthusiasm for the Laue experiment. They persevered, however, and set up an apparatus similar to the X-ray spectrometer. They verified the existence of the white radiation which had been postulated to explain the Laue photographs. They failed to discover the X-ray spectra, however, because in striving for accuracy they made the slits of collimator and chamber very fine, and missed the spectral lines in their survey. Moseley then heard of my father's work on spectra, and on repeating the experiments the missing lines were found. He resolved to go ahead with the exploration of spectra, while Darwin, who was a theoretical physicist, became interested in the mathematics of diffraction and produced two papers of the greatest importance on intensity of reflection which will be described in a later chapter.

To appreciate Moseley's work, one must consider it in relation to two major advances in Physics which were both made at Manchester at that time (1912). Rutherford had established the existence of the nucleus. He had interpreted the experiments of Geiger and Marsden on scattered α particles as proving the existence in an atom of a body which was responsible for nearly all its mass, and which carried a positive charge to balance the negative charge on the surrounding electrons. This hypothesis gave the right statistical distribution of the scattered α particles, and it was possible to determine roughly the nuclear charge. It proved to be the equivalent of about ten electronic charges in the case of aluminium, and about 100 charges in the case of gold.

Bohr had been developing his theory of spectra at Manchester. When he first came to England Bohr settled at Cambridge. I remember well a fellow student at Jeans' lectures on quantum theory who used to take me aside after the lecture and give me long dissertations on just where Jeans was wrong. This was Bohr—I little knew at the time how great a man was talking to me. He soon realized that the Mecca of physicists in England was at that time the school which had been inspired by Rutherford at Manchester, and he went to study there.

It was in this atmosphere that Moseley started his famous review of X-ray spectra, with the specific aim of testing Bohr's idea that they might in some way be analagous to light spectra.

2. The Moseley Spectrometer

Moseley published his results in two papers entitled 'The High Frequency Spectra of the Elements' in the *Philosophical Magazine*, in 1913 and 1914. The advance he made was to review the X-ray spectra

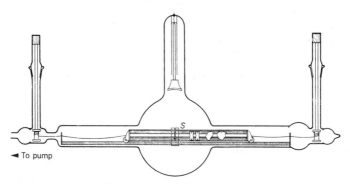

FIG. 1. Moseley's X-ray tube with interchangeable targets.

over a continuous range of elements, and this was made possible by a design of X-ray tube which was a very considerable technical achievement considering the apparatus available at that time.

This X-ray tube is illustrated in Fig. 1 taken from Moseley's paper. Targets of different metals were placed on the trolley, which could be moved along its track by winding cords around bobbins attached to the vacuum-tight taps shown in the figure. In this way each target could in turn be moved to a position where it came opposite the cathode and so gave out its characteristic X-rays. The radiations from some of the targets were in the very soft X-ray region, unable to penetrate even a window of aluminium, and therefore a window of goldbeaters skin was used through which the X-rays passed into the spectrometer. For the same reason, the air in the spectrometer was replaced by hydrogen which is less absorbent. The principle of the spectrometer is shown in Fig. 2. The X-rays from the anticathode pass through a narrow slit S. They fall on the cleavage face of a large crystal C, and are reflected onto the photographic plate L.

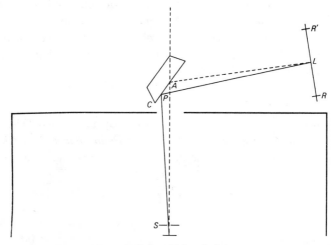

Fig. 2. The principle of Moseley's spectrometer.

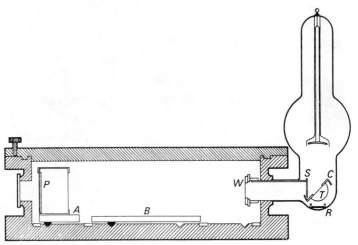

Fig. 3. The design of Moseley's spectrometer.

If the distances *SA*, *AL* are equal, then rays of the same wavelength are reflected to the point *L* by a mosaic element at any other point *P* on the crystal face, by the principle explained on page 40. When the crystal is turned, therefore, a spectrum of X-ray lines will be registered on the photographic plate, the wavelength of each being given by $n\lambda = 2d \sin \theta$ where θ is half the angle *SAL*. Moseley employed the cleavage face of a large crystal of potassium ferrocyanide which gives a strong third order reflection. The spacing corresponding to this reflection was measured by standardizing with the almost identical spacing of NaCl (200). The spectrometer is illustrated in Fig. 3.

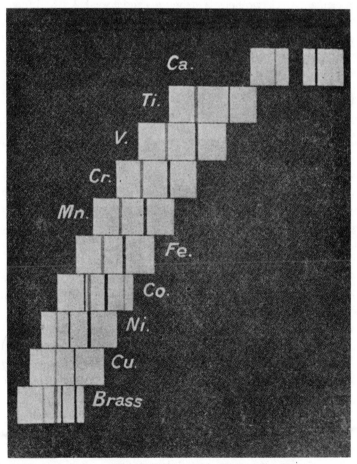

FIG. 4. X-ray spectra recorded photographically in Moseley's spectrometer for a range of elements from calcium to zinc.

Moseley first examined a range of elements from calcium to zinc, and obtained the famous picture shown in Fig. 4. Calcium gave considerable trouble, both because its radiation was so soft and because the lime which was used to provide a calcium target gave off so much gas that the tube could only be excited for a second or two at a time. Brass was used instead of zinc as anti-cathode because the latter volatilizes so readily. Some of the other metals were not pure and gave off lines of neighbouring elements; for instance the cobalt spectrum shows nickel and a trace of iron. The spectra are placed in register in the figures so that corresponding wavelengths are above each other, and the general run is quite clear. Each element gives two lines, a strong $K\alpha$ and a weak $K\beta$, and their lines form a regular progression from one element to the next. The jump between the lines of calcium and titanium is due to the omission of the element scandium in the series.

3. Atomic Number

Moseley later extended his investigations to a number of other elements, and also included the L spectra in his survey. Figure 5 sums up his results. My father had found that the frequencies of the K spectra were roughly proportional to the square of the atomic weight, so Moseley found it convenient to use the square roots of the frequencies as abscissae in Fig. 5. When these are plotted against the vertical series of elements, they lie very nearly on straight lines. One cannot do better than give the following quotations from Moseley's paper:

'We have here a proof that there is in the atom a fundamental quantity, which increases by regular steps as we pass from one element to the next. This quantity can only be the charge on the central positive nucleus, of the existence of which we already have definite proof.

We are therefore led by experiment to the view that N (i.e. the number of positive electronic charges on the nucleus) is the same as the number of the place occupied by the element in the periodic system. This atomic number is then for H, 1 for He, 2 for Li, 3 ... for Ca, 20 ... for Zn, 30, etc. This theory was originated by Broek and since used by Bohr. We can confidently predict that in the few cases in which the order of the atomic weights clashes with the chemical order of the periodic system, the chemical properties are governed by N, while A itself is probably a complicated function of N., The very close similarity between the X-ray spectra of the different elements shows that these radiations originate inside the atom, and have no direct connexion with the complicated light-spectra and chemical properties which are governed by the structure of its surface.

Soddy has pointed out that the chemical properties of the radio-elements are strong evidence that this hypothesis is true for the elements from thallium to uranium, so its general validity would now seem to be established.

Now if either the elements were not characterized by these integers, or any mistake had been made in the order chosen or the number of places left for unknown elements, these regularities would at once disappear. We can therefore conclude from the evidence of the X-ray spectra alone, without any theory of atomic structure, that these integers are really characteristic of the elements. Further, as it is improbable that two different stable elements should have the same integer, three, and only three, more elements are likely to exist between Al and Au. As the X-ray spectra of these elements can be confidently predicted, they should not be difficult to find.'

The gaps for the missing elements 43, 61 and 75 can be seen in Moseley's Fig. 5. Actually a fourth element, No. 72, was also absent (there was some confusion in the rare-earth region). These elements have now been discovered and identified by their X-ray spectra.

43 Technetium
61 Promethium
72 Hafnium
75 Rhenium

Although other experimental investigations and ideas current at the time greatly helped, Moseley fused them together into one grand scheme, and he will always be rightly regarded as the founder of 'Atomic Number'.

The other fundamental contribution made by Moseley was to link the X-ray spectra with Bohr's theory of optical spectra.

4. The Interpretation of X-ray Spectra

The simplest of all optical spectra is that emitted by atomic hydrogen, which is excited when the single electron is torn away from the nucleus by some catastrophe such as that caused by an electrical discharge. When the nucleus picks up an electron again, certain very regular series of lines are emitted. An empirical formula for the wave-numbers of these lines

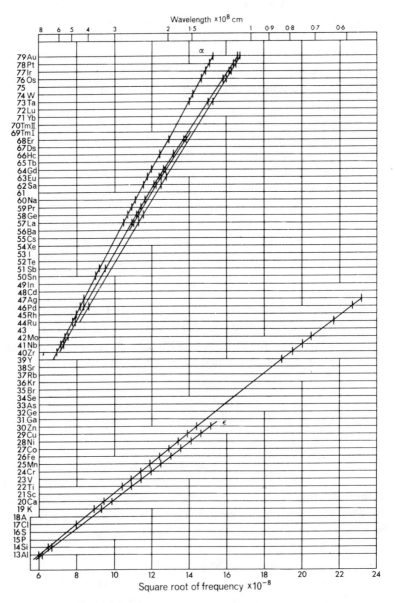

FIG. 5. X-rays spectra for the elements. After Moseley.

was found by Rydberg

$$N = N_o(1/n_1{}^2 - 1/n_2{}^2)$$

when N is the wave number (the number of waves in one centimetre in vacuo), N_0 is a constant called Rydberg's number, and n_1 and n_2 are integers. For instance, when n_1 is 2 and n_2 has the values 3, 4, 5, 6, etc. the formula gives the wave numbers of the Balmer series of hydrogen lines which starts in the visible region. If n_1 is one, and n_2 is 2, 3, 4, 5, it gives the Lyman series in the ultraviolet.

Bohr's great contribution was the realization that something which went beyond Newton's classical mechanics was essential to explain atomic structure and light emission. Previous attempts at explanation had treated the atom like a small machine obeying classical laws. Bohr realized that these attempts failed, not because the right model had not been found, but because in principle they were bound to fail.

Bohr introduced two new principles in approaching the problem. The first had really been already foreshadowed by Planck's Quantum Law and Einstein's treatment of the Photoelectric Effect. When energy is handed over from radiation to matter, or from matter to radiation, it is transferred in quanta given by the equation

$$E = h\nu$$

where E is the energy, ν is the frequency of the radiation, and h is a universal constant called Planck's constant (see page 37).

Bohr assumed that the same law governed the emission of spectra. A spectral line of definite frequency is emitted when the electron jumps from a 'state' of higher energy E_2 to another 'state' of lower energy E_1 according to the equation

$$h\nu = E_2 - E_1.$$

No radiation is emitted when the electron is in a quiescent state, it is only given out when a jump from one state to another takes place. The conception of a state is essential to an understanding of atomic structure. One of the stumbling blocks of applying classical ideas had been that, according to their principles, an electron rotating around a nucleus should emit radiation like any oscillating electrical system, so that the electron would lose energy and approach nearer to and revolve faster round the nucleus and finally fall into it, like a satellite caught in the earth's atmosphere. I remember Ehrenfest, at a Solvay conference when all these ideas were in the melting pot, declaring solemnly,

'Ze problem, vy the electron a pure ton geef, and not a noise like ze leet cat make'.

Bohr's assumption of states cut the Gordian Knot. They must exist to explain the definiteness of atomic structure.

Bohr then sought a rule for the states which would account for the spectra. It is very simple. The angular momentum of an electron in a steady state is a multiple of $h/2\pi$.

$$mvr = nh/2\pi$$

Combining this equation with that for equilibrium $mv^2/r = e^2/r^2$, and using the quantum condition, we find that the frequency of a spectral line due to a jump from orbit n_2 to orbit n_1 is

$$v = \{2\pi^2 me^4/h^3\}\cdot(1/n_1^2 - 1/n_2^2)$$

When this is expressed as wave numbers ($N = v/c$) and the values of m, e, h, and c the constant $2\pi^2 me^4/h^3 c$ proves to be identical with Rydberg's constant.

Moseley transferred this law to X-ray spectra. He showed that the K spectra of the elements were accounted for if one supposed that in exciting the X-rays an electron was torn away from an innermost position nearest the nucleus with its charge E, and an electron from a higher state jumped back to this position. The frequency for such a jump would then be

$$v = \left(\frac{1}{1^2} - \frac{1}{n^2}\right)\cdot 2\pi^2 e^2 E^2/h^3$$

Putting $n = 2$, and $E = (N-\sigma_n)e$ (when N is here the atomic number), the equation gives the frequencies of the $K\alpha$ lines of the elements. The reason for the effective charge being $(N-\sigma_n)e$ where σ_n is nearly unity, is that there are two electrons in the innermost orbit and so the single electron is returning to a nucleus with an approximate charge of $(N-1)e$.

Moseley therefore had shown that the X-ray spectra fall into line with optical spectra. To quote from his paper:

'This numerical agreement between the experimental values and those calculated from a theory designed to explain the ordinary hydrogen spectrum is remarkable, as the wave lengths dealt with in the two cases differ by a factor of about 2000.'

Moseley's work laid the foundation of X-ray spectroscopy. The measurement of X-ray wavelengths gave the binding energies of the electrons in the atom. These energies established the existence of the 'electron shells', the innermost of which has two electrons (the K shell), the next eight electrons (the L shell), and so forth. On this was based Bohr's explanation of the Periodic Table of the Elements. The $K\alpha$ line is produced by a jump from the L shell to an empty position in the K shell, the $K\beta$ line by a jump from M to K. The L spectra of the elements are produced by jumps from outer shells to an empty position in the L shell. An absorption edge represents the energy required to remove an electron from a shell.

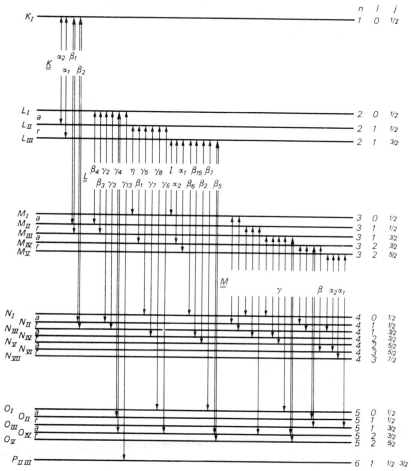

FIG. 6. Scheme of energy levels in uranium. (From *Spektroskopie der Röntgenstrahlen*, Siegbahn, Julius Springer.)

A very full survey of X-ray spectra of increased accuracy was made by M. Siegbahn and his school in Uppsala. Figure 6 shows diagrammatically the X-ray spectra emitted by the uranium atom. The horizontal lines represent the stationary states of electrons in the K, L, M, N, O, P shells and the vertical lines indicate the transitions from one state to another. The heights of the horizontal lines are not proportional to the actual energies involved; if they were the gap between K and L would be far larger than the gap between L and M, for instance.

The original Bohr picture of the atom was a mixture of new and classical mechanics which has been superseded by a more elegant and symmetrical theory, but this does not in any way alter Moseley's pioneer conception of the relation between optical and X-ray spectra.

CHAPTER 5

THE FIRST ANALYSIS OF CRYSTAL STRUCTURE

1. The Method of Analysis

Although the NaCl structure was deduced from Laue photographs, the first results with the X-ray spectrometer showed at once how far more powerful it was as an analytical tool. When I started work in the Leeds laboratory in the summer of 1913, my father was still mainly interested in exploring the X-ray spectra. It fell to me to use the spectrometer for determinations of crystalline arrangement and a number of inorganic structures were discovered. We wrote a joint paper on diamond and the other structures were described in a paper in the Royal Society Proceedings in 1913 which may be said to represent the start of X-ray crystallography.

It was very fortunate for me that I was able to work in my father's laboratory. Young research students nowadays can have little conception of the primitive conditions in a research laboratory some sixty years ago. The Cavendish Laboratory had about forty students trying to start research on problems suggested by the Professor J. J. Thomson. There was a workshop and a mechanic, Lincoln, but he could not possibly attend to the needs of such a large group and we all had to fend for ourselves. A box of tools containing a hammer, screwdriver, gimlet and so forth could be purchased by each student, and J. J. Thomson's assistant Everett gave lessons in elementary glass blowing. Odd pieces of wood and assorted tin cans were freely available, though glass and rubber tubing, mercury and insulated wire were jealously guarded and strictly rationed. There was only one foot pump for the glass-blowing blowpipe which we had to share as best we could. I remember how one of the lady researchers after a long wait had managed to get hold of the pump. Shortly afterwards she rashly left her door open on leaving her room, and when passing I saw the pump and bore it off. The next time I passed she was bowed over her desk in tears, but I regret to say I did not return the pump.

When I achieved the first X-ray reflections, I worked the Rumkorff coil too hard in my excitement and burnt out the platinum contact. Lincoln, the mechanic, was very annoyed as a contact cost ten shillings, and refused to provide me with another one for a month. In these days a researcher who discovered an effect of such novelty and importance would have very different treatment.

I could never have exploited my ideas about X-ray diffraction under such conditions. If some other laboratory than my father's had taken them up, my original work would have dropped out of the picture except perhaps for some brief mention. In my father's laboratory the facilities were on quite a different scale. He had never inherited the 'string and sealing wax' tradition of the Cavendish Laboratory, which dated from Rayleigh's time, because he had never worked there. When he first went to Adelaide as a Professor he found practically no apparatus in the Physics laboratory, and he apprenticed himself to a workshop in the town and learnt to use a metal lathe, so that he could make his own instruments. I think this gave him his love of good design. He tailored each piece of apparatus for the work it had to do, and at Leeds there was a good workshop with an excellent mechanic in charge to carry out his ideas. It was the privilege of working with really effective apparatus which made it possible for me to start my research career by working out a number of crystal structures.

The first structures were extremely simple by later standards (though they did not seem to be so at the time!), but they established a number of the main points of X-ray analysis. The spectral lines with which the measurements were made were the $K\alpha$ lines of palladium and rhodium, which are convenient because they stand out so strongly from the background of white radiation.

The analysis depended on comparing the strength of the various orders of reflection. When the planes are identical and evenly spaced, the orders fall off regularly; as a rough guide their relative intensities were taken to be in the ratio 100, 20, 5, 3, 1. A marked departure from this regular diminution indicated that the planes were not simple. Figure 1 taken from the original paper illustrates the point.

There are supposed to be two types of atomic sheets A and B, with reflecting powers m_1 and m_2. In Fig. 1(a) these sheets are coincident on planes with spacing D. In Fig. 1(b) the B sheet has been shifted by a distance D/n. There will now be a phase difference between the waves reflected from the composite sheets, which will be $2\pi h/n$ for the order

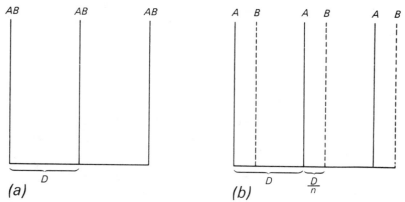

FIG. 1. Interplanar spacing for structures with two types of atoms. (*a*) atom types A and B coincident on planes with spacing D; (*b*) atoms type B shifted by a distance D/n.

(h), so the intensity will be reduced from $(m_1+m_2)^2$ to $m_1^2+m_2^2+2m_1m_2\cos(2\pi h/n)$. The amplitudes must be vectorially compounded and the intensity is proportion to the square of the amplitude; of course the same holds true for more complex cases. This is the fundamental optical principle of X-ray analysis.

An initial step in all the analyses is the determination of the number of atoms in the unit cell. The volume of this cell is found from the angle of reflection of X-rays of known wavelength. If there are n units of molecular weight M in the unit cell of volume V, then

$$nMm = \varrho V$$

where m is the mass of a hydrogen atom, and ϱ is the density of the crystal. This determines n.

For historical interest, the structures are illustrated by the original figures.

2. Diamond

The measurements showed that diamond is based on a face-centred cubic lattice, and that two carbon atoms are associated with each point of the lattice. There were two significant features of the reflections. For the cube face, 200 and 600 were missing, while 400, 800 etc. appeared in full strength. The reflection 222 was missing, while 111, 333, 444 and 555 were present. This peculiar feature of the 111 reflections is shown in Fig. 2.

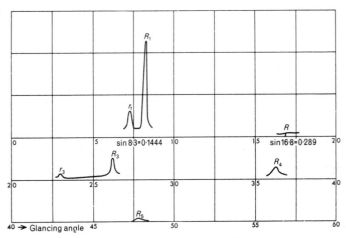

FIG. 2. X-ray reflections from diamond.

The structure which explained these features is shown in Fig. 3. One set of carbon atoms A lies on the points of a face-centred cubic lattice. The others B lie on a similar lattice which is displaced along the cube diagonal by a distance of $\frac{1}{4}$ of this diagonal. The effect of the displacement

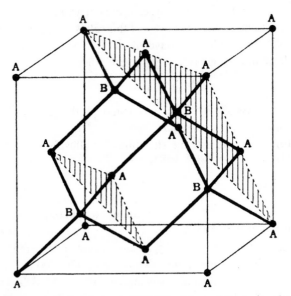

FIG. 3. Structure of diamond. Successive 111 planes of the unit cube have been shaded.

is that each carbon atom has four arranged around it at the corners of a regular tetrahedron. The structure is shown in Fig. 3.

The absence of the 222 reflection is explained by the structure of the (111) planes which is illustrated by Fig. 3. The carbon planes divide the (111) spacing in the ratio 1 : 3, or in other words their relative displacement is $\pi/2$, and so the contributions to 222 are in opposite phase and cancel out, thus accounting for the absence of this reflection.

The analysis of diamond aroused great interest and had a major effect is emphasizing the power of this new method of analysis, not only because of the direct way in which the structure explained the spectra but also because it was such an elegant illustration of the tetrahedrally arranged four bonds of a carbon atom.

3. Inorganic Structures

The original measurements on several crystals are shown in Table 1.

TABLE 1

Rock salt, Pd rays—					
(100)	100 11·7°	30 23·8°	7 36·2°		
(110)	100 16·5°	34 34·0°	7 52·0°		
(111)	20 10·2°	100 20·6°	0 —	6 42·5°	
Fluorspar, Pd rays—					
(100)	0 —	100 24·5°	0 —	13 50·5°	
(110)	100 17·4°	16 35·4°	6 51·5°		
(111)	100 10·7°	0 21·5°	10 32·5°	9 43·7°	3 53·5°
Zincblende, Rh rays—					
(100)	40 12·8°	100 25·9°	0		
(110)	100 18·2°	25 37·2°	7 57·5°		
(111)	100 11·4°	5 23·0°	8 34·7°		
Pyrites, Rh rays—					
(100)	100 13·0°	0 26·2°	0 39·6°	14 53·8°	4 69·0°
(110)	100 18·1°	50 37·2°	0 —		
(110)	80 11·4°	100 22·6°	50 34·2°	0 —	22 58·8°

Rock Salt, NaCl. Because the lattice is face-centred cubic, only reflections with indices which are all odd or all even appear. In the former case the reflections from the Na sheets are in opposite phase to those from the Cl

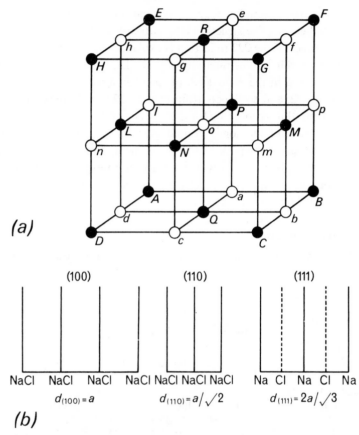

FIG. 4. Structure and arrangement of planes in sodium chloride.

sheets, so the 'all odd' spectra are weak compared with the 'all even' (Fig. 4 and p. 29).

Fluorspar, CaF₂. The calcium atoms lie on a face-centred cubic lattice, the fluorine atoms occupy positions at the centre of the small cubes as in diamond, but now all the centres are occupied because there are two fluorine atoms for every calcium atom. The consequence is sets of planes with the structure illustrated in Fig. 5. The effect on the spectra is similar to that in the case of diamond—200, 600 etc., and 222, are absent. In this case, however, the disappearance of the spectra is due to the equal reflecting power of the two atoms of fluorine of atomic weight 19, and one of calcium of atomic weight 40. The equality confirms and carries further

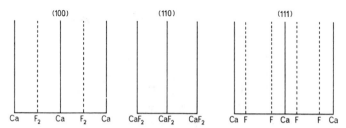

Fig. 5. Arrangement of planes in fluorspar.

the rule that the scattering power of an atom is approximately proportional to its atomic weight.

Zincblende, ZnS. The structure in Fig. 6(*a*) shows the similarities with diamond and fluor spar. The zinc atoms are on one cubic face-centred lattice, and the sulphur atoms on another at the centres of the small cubes. The 222 spectrum is weak, but is present because S is a lighter atom than Zn and does not completely balance it.

The structure was of particular interest when it was discovered because it was the first example of a crystal having hemihedral or less than full cubic symmetry. The crystals have the symmetry of a tetrahedron such as that shown in Fig. 6(*b*), not the complete symmetry of a cube, and this is explained by the structure. The (111) planes shown in Fig. 6(*a*) are *polar*, having pairs of sheets ZnS—ZnS—. Hence, for instance, there will be a different rate of growth of (111) and ($\overline{1}\overline{1}\overline{1}$) and the crystal may assume forms like the crystal of tetrahedrite (Fig. 6(*b*)).

Pyrites, FeS₂. The solution of pyrites was very interesting for several reasons. It is based on iron atoms on a face-centred cubic lattice. The spectra show at once, however, that the sulphur atoms are in no such simple position as the fluorine atoms in CaF_2. If that had been the case one would expect 400 and 800 to be strong, and 200 and 600 to be weak. In marked contrast 200 is strong, 400 and 600 are weak, and 800 and 10,0,0 are strong. This was an enigma, because the positions of F in CaF_2, or S in ZnS or C in diamond are fixed by their lying on intersecting three-fold axes and the atom cannot move from the centre of the small cube without destroying the symmetry.

I remember so well finding the answer to this conundrum when poring over an old paper by Pope and Barlow, and realizing by an example they gave that it was possible to have a system of non-intersecting three-

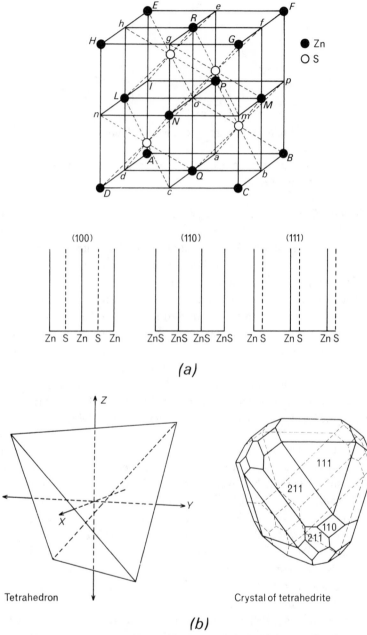

FIG. 6. (*a*) Structure and arrangement of planes in zincblende; (*b*) tetrahedral symmetry of zincblende crystal.

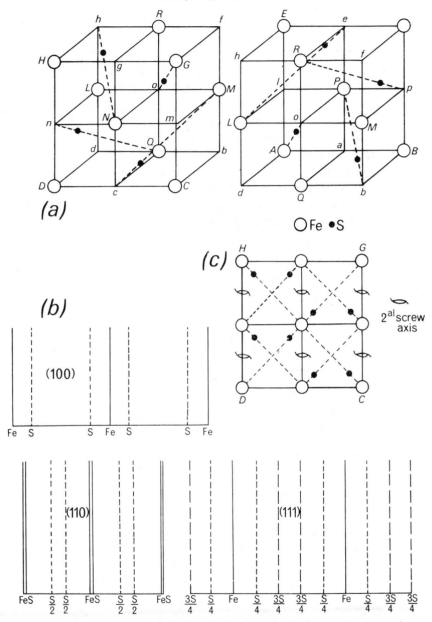

FIG. 7. (a) The cubical unit cell of the FeS_2 structure, the front and rear section are shown separately in order to make the arrangement more clear;

(b) Arrangement of planes in FeS_2 structure;

(c) Arrangement of symmetry elements.

fold axes in a cubic crystal. Such a system is shown in Fig. 7. Each sulphur atom lies on only one of these trigonal axes, and it is now possible for it to be moved anywhere along the axis; it need not be at the centre of the cube. Here for the first time one was dealing with a new feature of the crystal structure, the parameter. In previous cases the precise position of each atom had been fixed by the symmetry elements (see Chapter 6).

The intensities of the spectra were explained by a shift of the sulphur atom along a threefold axis towards the empty corner so that its distance from the corner is about one-fifth of the dotted diagonal (a later measurement, made with the full panoply of accurate intensity determination, indicated a displacement of 0.23 rather than 0.20).

This structure explains the type of hemihedral cubic symmetry shown by FeS_2, which is illustrated in Fig. 8. These crystals often grow as cubes, and the cube faces have striations which are perpendicular to

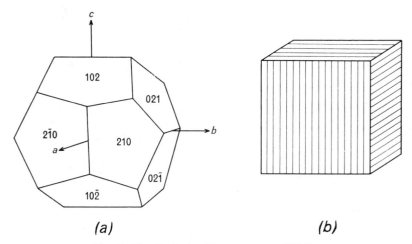

(a)   (b)

FIG. 8. Hemihedral cubic symmetry of FeS_2.

each other on adjoining faces, as in Fig. 8(b). In the crystal form of Fig. 8(a), the faces (210) and (210) have developed, but not the faces (120) and (120), so that the axes of symmetry shown by the arrows are twofold, not fourfold. Fig. 7(c) shows the projection of the unit cell on a cube face. The pairs of S atoms in this case are horizontal, but if one turns the model through a right angle they become vertical (Fig. 9). It can be shown that the striations on the cube faces are parallel to the pairs of sulphur atoms. The structures of the planes (2$\overline{1}$0) and (120) are different, which explains the development of the one and not the other in Fig. 8(a).

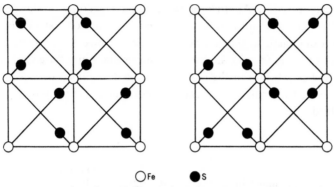

○ Fe   ● S

FIG. 9. Structure of pyrites, FeS$_2$, projected upon two adjacent cube faces.

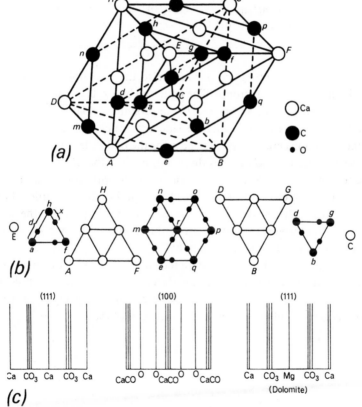

FIG 10. (*a*) Atomic arrangement in crystals of the calcite series;
(*b*) distribution of atoms in individual sheets;
(*c*) arrangement of planes in the calcite structure.

The Calcite series. Another of the pioneer structures is illustrated in Fig. 10. The structure may be compared with that of NaCl compressed along a diagonal, so that the edges of the cell meet at an angle of 102° instead of being at right angles. The cations and anions are Ca and CO_3 groups. The position of the oxygen atom is determined by a parameter, and the best fit with the spectra indicates that x/d (Fig. 10(b)) is about one-third.

TABLE 2

	(111)	(222)
Sodium Nitrate, Na(23).NO_3(62)	100	50
Dolomite (Ca,Mg)(32).CO_3(60)	100	100
Calcite Ca(40).CO_3(60)	30	100
Rhodochrosite Mn(54).CO_3(60)	0	100
Chalybite Fe(56).CO_3(60)	0	100

The sheets of atoms perpendicular to the three-fold axis are alternately cations and CO_3 groups. The figures in brackets in Table 2 show the atomic weights of the sheets and the approximate relative intensities of 111 and 222 in a series of structures similar to calcite. Their contributions to the reflections are in opposite phase for the odd orders and in the same phase for the even orders. Sodium nitrate has the same structure as calcite, and dolomite a similar structure but with equal numbers of magnesium and calcium atoms. It will be seen that the first order diminishes relatively to the second as the cation layers approach the anion layers in total weight, a further proof that scattering power is approximately proportional to atomic weight.

This old story has been recounted in some detail, not only for its historic interest as a first step in the development of X-ray analysis, but also because these early ventures established main principles in a way which is easy to follow owing to the simplicity of the structures.

CHAPTER 6

SYMMETRY

1. The Space Lattice

Crystals are three-dimensional patterns. It is the regular arrangement of the atoms, like soldiers drawn up on parade, that constitutes a crystalline solid as distinct from an amorphous body in which there is no such regularity. Crystals must obey certain laws of symmetry which govern three-dimensional patterns of any kind. The symmetry scheme of a crystalline structure can be deduced from its diffraction of X-rays, and its determination is an essential first step in analysis.

If one's eye roves over a two-dimensional pattern, like that of a wallpaper or a curtain, it is possible to see that the pattern repeats at definite intervals both to right and left, and up and down. If the pattern contains a rosebud, for instance, there will be precisely similar rosebuds with exactly the same surroundings at these intervals. The designer often tries to disguise the rather dull feature of this repeat by interposing other rosebuds of almost the same shape, so as to tire the eye out in looking for similarity and to make one believe that nothing is exactly alike, but the demand of printing a continuous pattern makes repeats unavoidable.

Any series of similar points lies on a lattice. It does not matter which point is chosen; the lattice is shifted but always has the same shape.

The corresponding scheme in three dimensions is called a *space lattice* (Fig. 1). Axes of the lattice are defined by joining a point to three neighbouring points which are not in a plane, and a *unit cell* is formed by completing the box. The way in which this is done is arbitrary. The dotted lines in Fig. 1 show a simple way of outlining the unit cell, with sides that are not too far from being at right angles, but they could also be drawn in other ways such as those shown by the full lines. Since each corner of a cell is shared by eight other cells, and there are eight corners, there is one point of the lattice to each cell. A unit cell is described by the lengths of its sides (a, b and c) and the angles between them (α, β and γ).

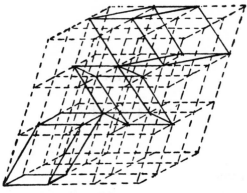

Fɪɢ. 1. The space lattice showing alternative ways of outlining the unit cell.

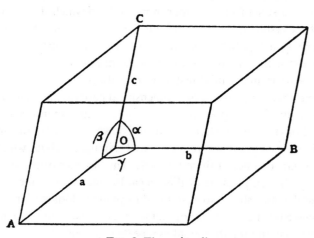

Fɪɢ. 2. The unit cell.

It is sometimes convenient to use unit cells which are not simple, in that they contain more than one point of the lattice, in order to show the full symmetry of the lattice. In Fig. 3 all three unit cells outlined heavily are cells of a space lattice which has three equal axes OA OB OC making equal angles with each other. When these angles are right angles the result is a simple cubic lattice (*a*). If the angles are 60°, the resulting lattice also has cubic symmetry, but now with points at the corners and face centres of a cube, so that there are four points to each unit cell. If the angle is 109° 28′ the lattice is also cubic, the cube in this case having a point at its centre and two points to the unit cell. (sec Fig. 9, p. 24).

There are thus three space lattices with cubic symmetry. A list of other possible schemes shows that altogether 14 types are possible shown in Fig. 4 based on seven crystal systems. (1) is *triclinic*, with three unequal axes and angles. Numbers (2) and (3) are *monoclinic*, in which two of the angles are right angles. It is easy to see that this condition can be obeyed when the (001) face is centred as well as when the points are only at

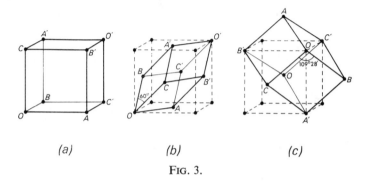

(a)   (b)   (c)

Fig. 3.

corners. The rest of the lattices are *orthorhombic* (4, 5, 6, 7), *hexagonal* (8), *rhombohedral* (9), *tetragonal* (10, 11), and *cubic* (12, 13, 14). The list is complete; for instance, although a tetragonal lattice could have points at the centres of all the faces, like the cubic lattice 14, this is not another type. If one turns the 'a' axes round through 45°, it becomes a body-centred lattice like 11.

It is convenient to denote these lattices by single-letter symbols. The simple lattice has the symbol P (primitive); the lattice centred on one face only has the symbol A, B or C describing centring on the (100), (010) or (001) faces respectively; the all-face-centred lattice has the symbol F; and the body-centred lattice has the symbol I (innenzentriert). It is also usual to denote the hexagonal lattice by H and the rhombohedral lattice by R, although they are both primitive.

In principle, the edges of a unit cell can be labelled *a*, *b* and *c* in any way relative to the symmetry, but certain conventions are now well established. For hexagonal and tetragonal unit cells the edge that is different in length from the other two is labelled *c*, but for monoclinic unit cells the unique axis—that which is perpendicular to the plane of the other two—is called *b*.

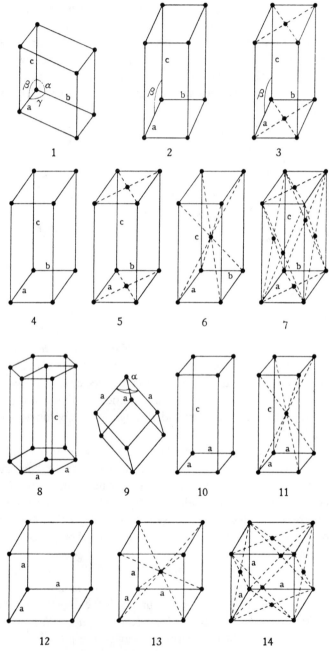

FIG. 4. The fourteen space lattices.

2. Symmetry of the Pattern

It will be noticed that the symmetry only runs in ones, twos, threes, fours and sixes. Fives, sevens and higher numbers are ruled out because one cannot fit cells with such symmetries together. The existence of seven crystal systems expresses this limitation. For example, twofold symmetry, denoted by the symbol 2, means that the unit cell must have exactly the same appearance after each of two half-rotations (180°). This can happen only if the axis of this rotation is in the plane perpendicular to the other two axes; that is, the crystal is monoclinic. Similarly, if the unit cell is a rectangular parallelopiped, the crystal must have mutually perpendicular twofold axes of rotation. But it may also have another type of symmetry —the mirror plane—denoted by the symbol *m*. One half of the unit cell can be regarded as the mirror image of the other half.

These symmetries are those of clusters of atoms, identical in form and orientation, associated with each point of the lattice as in the pattern of wallpaper or fabrics. How many types of symmetry may these patterns have? The number is limited geometrically, just as the number of possible regular solids is limited, or the number of space lattices. The answer was found independently by Federov, Schoenflies and Barlow; there are 230 different schemes of pattern symmetry in three dimensions.

At first sight this seems a large number, and Fig. 5 may help to show why there are so many possibilities. The symmetries of ten types of ortho-rhombic pattern are illustrated in this figure. The nature of the symmetry in all ten types is such that the pattern is the same to right and left, and is also the same back and front. The vertical *c* axis is supposed to be polar; that is, its properties in one direction are different from its properties in the other: we may picture the triangles in the figures to be black on top and white underneath to show that up and down are not the same. The patterns are all based on a simple orthorhombic lattice (Fig. 4) with points at the corners of a rectangular cell.

Mirror planes and glide planes. The simplest way to achieve the equivalence of back-to-front and right-to-left is to have mirror planes perpendicular to *a* and *b* so that there are four triangles around each lattice point as in the first example *Pmm*.

The same equivalence is also attained but in another way in the next example, *Pmc*.

There are again mirror planes perpendicular to *a*, but the planes perpendicular to *b* are *glide planes*, denoted by the symbol *c*. A glide plane

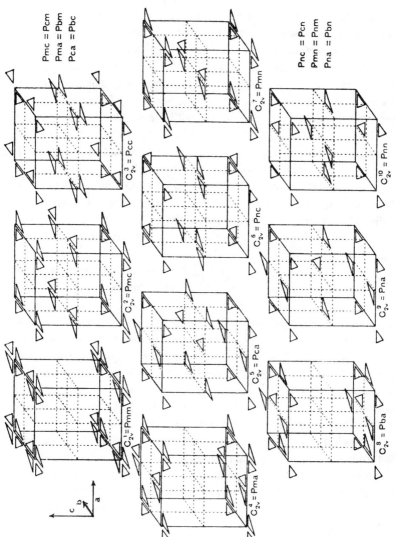

FIG. 5. The ten space groups of the orthorhombic polar class, based upon a primitive lattice.

involves two operations—reflection and translation of a simple fraction of a lattice translation, in this case $\frac{1}{2}c$. The reason why glide planes are possible is that the basic property of a symmetry element is that it must, after a limited number of operations, leave the atomic arrangement looking exactly the same as at the beginning. Two operations of reflection, m, bring every atom exactly back to its original site. Two operations of a glide plane, c, bring every atom to the same place in an adjacent unit cell. Since all unit cells are identical, this is just as satisfactory as bringing an atom back to where it originally was.

All the possibilities of combinations of two planes—mirrors and glides—are shown in Fig. 5: in every case there are four triangles in all four orientations required by the symmetry but the triangles are related in a different way.

To those possibilities must be added similar series for the other three kinds of orthorhombic lattice (Fig. 4): all give the same right-to-left, and front-to-back, symmetry. This example illustrates how the large number of 230 space groups comes about by permutations of symmetry elements.

Rotation axes and screw axes. As is seen in the diagrams of space lattices in Fig. 4 it is possible to have one-fold, two-fold, three-fold, four-fold, or six-fold axes in three-dimensional patterns. A rotation axis brings the pattern into coincidence again by making one half, one third, one quarter or one sixth of a complete turn. The symmetry axis may, however, be a *screw axis*, which makes a fraction of a turn combined with a translation along its length. Like the glide plane, the screw axis also, after a small number of operations, moves an atom into a neighbouring unit cell. The six possible types of hexagonal screw axis are shown in Fig. 6. In the first, denoted by 6_1, the axis turns 0 into 1 and so on by making a sixth of a turn combined with a translation downwards of one sixth of the lattice spacing, moving like a corkscrew being screwed into a cork. In 6_2 the translation is one third of the axis, in 6_3 one half. 6_4 and 6_5 are screws in the other sense and 6 is a plain rotation.

Centres of inversion and axes of rotatory inversion. A crystal pattern may have *centres of inversion* or symmetry centres. Each point of the pattern is matched by a similar one at an equal distance on the opposite side of the centre.

There is one other type of symmetry it may possess—an *axis of*

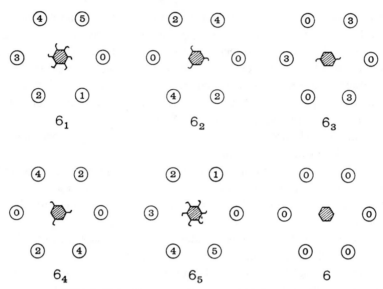

FIG. 6. The different types of hexagonal screw axes.

rotatory inversion. The movement consists of rotation about an axis combined with inversion about a centre on the axis. Such axes are denoted by $\bar{1}$ (a simple inversion), $\bar{2}$ (equivalent to a reflection), $\bar{3}$, $\bar{4}$, $\bar{6}$.

The possible axes therefore are

$$6, 6_1, 6_2, 6_3, 6_4, 6_5 \text{ and } \bar{6}$$

$$4, 4_1, 4_2, 4_3 \text{ and } \bar{4}$$

$$3, 3_1, 3_2 \text{ and } \bar{3}$$

$$2, 2_1 \text{ and } \bar{2} (= m)$$

$$1 \text{ and } \bar{1}.$$

As in the case of symmetry planes, the possible permutations of these types of axis must all be taken into account in listing the varieties of crystal symmetry.

3. Space Groups

The three-dimensional assemblage of planes, axes, and centres of symmetry is called a *space group*. It must be self-consistent, so that any symmetry operation of the space group turns the whole group into co-i ncidence again. One can think of this assemblage as being like the mirrors of a kaleidoscope, which turn an irregular collection of objects into an attractive repeated pattern. If an atom is placed at any point in the space group, the symmetry elements multiply it into the similar atoms all through the structure.

The nomenclature of the space group. A very ingenious nomenclature of the space groups was first devised by Hermann and simplified by ¦Mauguin. A few standard symbols not only define the space group, but also when necessary the relation of the symmetry elements to the way the axes have been chosen. The first letter, as we have seen in section 1, defines the space lattice. The symbols which follow denote the types of symmetry axes and symmetry planes of the structure. The nomenclature of the axes has already been given. For planes, m denotes a reflection (mirror plane), a, b, c are glide planes with translations $a/2$, $b/2$, $c/2$, n is a plane with a translation of half a face-diagonal. A detailed example of an orthorhombic space group is given in a later section of this chapter.

4. The Crystal Class

Before the advent of X-ray analysis it was not possible to discover the space group of the pattern in a crystal and the only clue one had to its nature was the symmetry shown by the shape of the crystal and by its physical properties. These symmetry properties divided crystals into 32 classes, shown in Fig. 7. The reason why the classes are so few in number as compared with the 230 space groups is because it is not possible to distinguish between mirror planes and glide planes, or between rotation axes and screw axes, by means of the external form. Their effect on the shape of the crystal is just the same. Any of the ten space groups shown in Fig. 5, for example, might belong to No. VII in Miers' series (Fig. 7). The crystal classes were important to classical crystallography, and their forms led to theoretical explanations of them based on the theory of space groups. In X-ray analysis, however, it is the space group which is important, the crystal form being only a secondary effect.

5. The Determination of Space Groups by X-ray Diffraction

A first step in X-ray analysis is the determination of the space group governing the pattern of the crystal. This can be done by surveying the whole body of reflections and noting any peculiarities about their sets of indices.

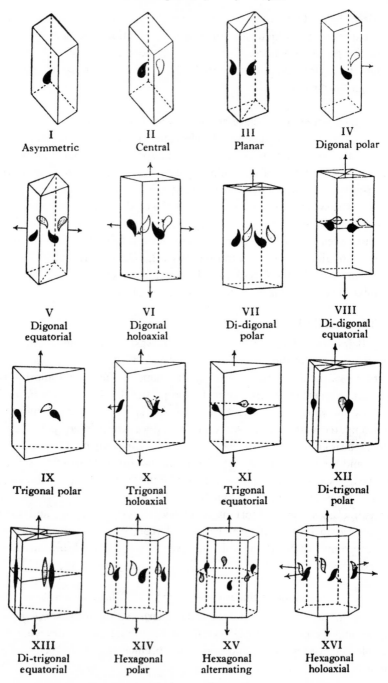

FIG. 7. The 32 classes of crystal symmetry.

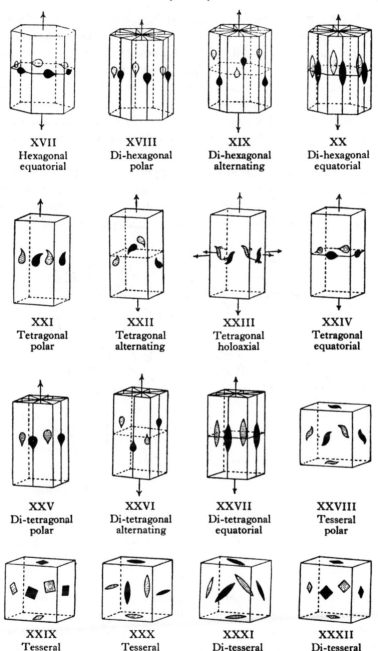

XVII	XVIII	XIX	XX
Hexagonal equatorial	Di-hexagonal polar	Di-hexagonal alternating	Di-hexagonal equatorial

XXI	XXII	XXIII	XXIV
Tetragonal polar	Tetragonal alternating	Tetragonal holoaxial	Tetragonal equatorial

XXV	XXVI	XXVII	XXVIII
Di-tetragonal polar	Di-tetragonal alternating	Di-tetragonal equatorial	Tesseral polar

XXIX	XXX	XXXI	XXXII
Tesseral holoaxial	Tesseral central	Di-tesseral polar	Di-tesseral central

In the first place, having established the unit cell, one can decide the type of space lattice. In the case of a simple lattice with a point at each corner of the unit cell, all values of *hkl* are possible. Some reflections may be so weak that they cannot be registered, but there will be no systematic absences in the sets of indices. If, however, the space lattice has more than one point to the unit cell, certain families of indices will be absent. If the lattice is body-centred, $h+k+l$ must be even. If it is face-centred, *h*, *k* and *l* must be all even or all odd. If the (100) face alone is centred, then $k+l$ must be even and correspondingly for (010) and (001). By looking for systematic absences of this kind which apply to all the spectra, one can uniquely determine the lattice. The measurements, of course, also give the dimensions of the unit cell and so, with the density, the number of atoms in it. Figure 8 shows how a mirror plane and glide plane can be distingui-

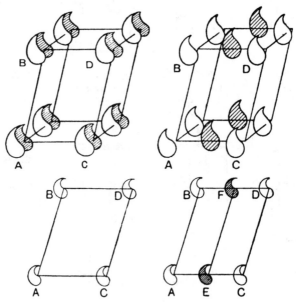

FIG. 8. Absent spectra owing to glide plane.

shed. The structure on the right has a plane with a glide $a/2$, *a* being the horizontal axis. Viewed along the 'c' direction, which is at right angles to the *ab* plane, the 'a' axis is halved in length in the projection, so for the reflecting planes parallel to the 'c' axis, the axes are effectively $a/2$ and *b*. Hence in the sets of reflections with indices *hk0*, *h* must always be even.

If the glide plane has a translation $b/2$, k must be even and if it is a glide plane n then $h+k$ must be even. On the other hand, when the structure has a mirror plane, as on the left, there are no restrictions to the values.

When an axis is screw, there is a restriction on the indices of reflecting planes perpendicular to the axis. For instance if there is a 3_1 or 3_2 axis parallel to 'c' as in quartz the only reflections will be of the third order, sixth order, ninth order and so forth. This is so because the structure of these planes depends only on the coordinates of the atoms parallel to c, and these are repeated three times in the length of the unit cell by the action of the screw axis. Very frequently crystals have a 2_1 axis parallel to a principal axis, 'a' for instance, and in such a case only 200, 400, 600 will appear, the odd spectra being absent.

The detection of a centre of symmetry is more subtle and will be dealt with in a subsequent chapter when intensity of reflection is considered. Briefly, crystals with a centre of symmetry have a greater proportion of reflections which are small than is the case for crystals without a centre, and a statistical survey of the reflections reveals the presence or absence of a centre of symmetry.

To sum up:

(a) The space lattice is deduced from the spectra with general indices *hkl*. A systematic absence of certain spectra indicates that the unit cell which has been chosen contains more than one point of the lattice.

(b) Glide planes are distinguished by systematic absences in a zone of reflections, that is a set of reflections with one index zero.

(c) Screw axes are distinguished by certain orders being missing for planes perpendicular to the axes, that is among a set of reflections with two indices zero.

(d) Centres of inversion or symmetry centres are deduced from a statistical survey of the strong and weak reflections.

6. Example of a Space Lattice

An example of an orthorhombic space lattice is shown in Fig. 9. The operations of the space lattice turn an atom such as 1 in the figure into eight atoms in all. The unit cell is primitive. There are mirror planes perpendicular to 'b' shown as heavy lines which turn 1 into 2. The glide planes shown as dotted lines are perpendicular to a with a glide $b/2+c/2$, and these turn the pair 1, 2 into the pair 3, 4. The glide planes perpendicular to *c*, and so parallel to the plane of the diagram, have a translation *a*/2 and turn 1, 2 into 4′3′, and 3, 4 into 1′, 2′. So the space group notation for this structure is *Pnma*. The structure has other elements of symmetry. There are screw axes parallel to *a*, *b* and *c*, as shown in the figure. Centres of inversion are shown as stars. It is not necessary to include symbols for these elements in the space-group notation, because they are a

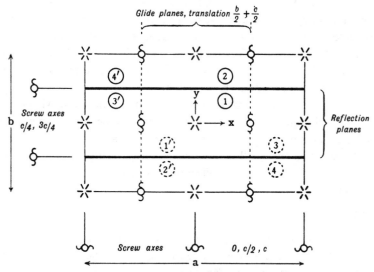

FIG. 9. The symmetry elements of the space group *Pnma* and the set of equivalent atoms in a general position.

necessary consequence of the mirror and glide planes. It is an advantage of the Hermann–Mauguin notation that it not only gives the symmetries but also shows how they are related to the axes which have been chosen. In this case the order of the symbols shows that the *n* plane is perpendicular to *a*, the *m* mirror plane to *b*, and the glide plane *a* to *c*. Alternative notations would be *Pnam, Pbnm, Pbmn, Pmnb, Pmcn*; these indicate the same space group but the set up of the axes is different.

The rules for determining space groups were first outlined by Niggli in Germany, and further tables were published by Wyckoff in America and Astbury and Yardley (later Professor Lonsdale) in Great Britain. The early structures to be analysed were so simple that their symmetries could easily be found in an *ad hoc* way, but as more complex crystals came to be examined the tables became the guide to an essential first step in X-ray analysis.

CHAPTER 7

THE INTENSITY OF REFLECTION

1. The Quantitative Problem

Very crude methods of estimating the relative intensities of the different spectra were used in the early analyses. When the structure only had one or two parameters, these measurements sufficed to assign surprisingly accurate positions to the atoms. The calculated intensities for the higher orders of spectra vary very rapidly with small changes of atomic position, and it was easy to fix the parameters within narrow limits by a comparison with experiment. As more complex crystals were investigated, with a number of parameters to be determined, these approximate methods were incapable of giving answers, and it became essential to treat the diffraction in a quantitative, not a qualitative, way.

Chapter 4, in describing the first analyses, outlines the general principles. The pattern of atoms in the unit cell scatters strongly in some directions and weakly in others, owing to interference of the wavelets scattered by the atoms. If the *hkl* spectrum is in a direction of strong scattering it will be strong, and vice-versa. One can check whether one has assumed a structure which is correct by comparing the calculated strength of scattering with the observed intensities of the spectra.

The problem can perhaps be understood more readily if the aim of a rigorous quantitative comparison is defined. The unit cell contains a certain number N of electrons which scatter wavelets. If all these were in phase the amplitude of the scattered wave would be N times as great as that due to a single electron. This is the case for scattering through zero angle, but in other directions the amplitude is reduced by interference to a lower values $F(hkl)$. This quantity $F(hkl)$ may be thought of as the measure of the scattering efficiency of the unit cell, measured in electron scattering as unit. It is a ratio, a pure number. *The establishment of values of F(hkl) is the ultimate aim of all methods of measurement, and all calculations of crystal structure are based on them.*

2. Darwin's Formulae

The formulae for deriving values of $F(hkl)$ from experimental measurements were deduced by C. G. Darwin in two remarkable papers in 1914. They were remarkable because they have been the basis of all subsequent X-ray measurement, although they were established at such an early stage before they could be applied in any complete way to experimental results. As well as devising a very ingenious mathematical analysis, they showed a great insight into the physical nature of a crystal.

The derivation of the formulae for intensity of reflection by a given crystalline arrangement is a somewhat complex problem of optics which it is not necessary to go into here; it will be found in any text book. However, the physical significance of the results will be described in some detail, because of its vital importance.

The analysis starts with the efficiency of scattering by a single electron, given by the standard electro-magnetic formula. From this one can calculate the f value, the relative efficiency of scattering at any angle by the group of electrons in each atom, and then combine these values into the resultant $F(hkl)$ for all the atoms in the unit cell. Next, one considers a single sheet (hkl) of these scattering units, and calculates the fraction of amplitude A/A_0 which is reflected when an X-ray wave of amplitude A_0 crosses the plane.

This calculation is straightforward and rigorous, and there is no question of its validity. The difficulties set in when one calculates how these waves, coming from the successive crystal planes, combine together to form the resultant diffracted wave.

The perfect crystal. Darwin started by postulating that the crystal is quite perfect. He supposed waves to be falling on the face of a crystal which was parallel to the reflecting planes. As the reflection builds up by successive planes making their contributions, there will be at any point inside the crystal a wave of amplitude T in the direction of the incident wave, and one of amplitude S in the direction of the reflected wave. We have to consider not only the increase in S due to the reflection of T in crossing each plane as we go deeper, but also the contribution to T because a part of S is reflected back again in the T direction. Darwin solved the 'difference equations' involved, and got the relation between the incident wave T_0 and reflected wave S_0.

In considering the answer, one relationship is of importance. For a typical case of reflection the fraction of amplitude reflected at a single crystal plane is of the order of 10^{-4}, whereas the amplitude lost by absorption is of the order of 10^{-6}, one hundred times less.

The net result of the calculation is that over a short range of angle, of a few seconds of arc, the reflection is effectively 100%. One can see physically why this is the case. The ray T will continue to plunge into the crystal, getting weaker by its loss to S, until after a few thousand planes it becomes negligibly small. Since no energy is mopped up by absorption, all the incident energy must reappear as reflected energy. The amplitudes add only as long as the contributions from the lower planes are sufficiently near in phase to those in the upper planes. If the angle is wrong by more than a few seconds of arc this ceases to be true and so there is no reflection except over a very narrow range. The X-ray absorption has no effect.

The ideally imperfect crystal. Darwin realized that this equation did not correspond with observation in two ways. In the first place, the measured reflection was far stronger than would be accounted for by reflection only taking place over an angle of a few seconds, even if it were perfect over this range. In the second place, the absorption by the crystal has a major effect on the reflection, as had been shown by my father's results on the effect of the crystal constituents on the platinum peaks (page 37). There must be something wrong in the physical assumptions and Darwin realized that the error lay in assuming the crystal to be perfect.

The opposite extreme to assuming that the crystal is as perfect as it possibly can be is to assume that it is as irregular as it can possibly be, and this assumption gives the correct formula! Such a crystal is termed an 'Ideally Imperfect Crystal'. It is supposed to be composed of a mosaic of crystal elements in slightly different orientation due to faults in crystal growth or subsequent strains. Each element is so small that the X-ray amplitude is reduced by only a fraction in crossing it. To put it in another way, the number of crystal planes traversed in any mosaic element is far smaller than that required to build up the 100% reflection of the perfect crystal.

At first sight is seems paradoxical that an imperfect crystal should give a stronger reflection than a perfect crystal, but the reason is simple. Suppose we are considering the reflection of a narrow X-ray beam, and measuring the integrated reflection as the crystal is swept uniformly through the reflecting position, which is the only way of making a significant measurement (page 41). The perfect crystal reflects over a few seconds of arc only, and outside this range there is nothing. The beam falling on the imperfect crystal, however, can at each setting dive down into the crystal till it meets a mosaic element orientated correctly for reflection, the effect only being weakened at greater depths by absorption. The crystal reflects over a range which depends on the scatter of the mosaic orientations, and which may be a degree or so of arc. At any one angle the reflection is much less than 100% as for the perfect crystal, but the integrated reflection is much greater.

To quote the actual basic formula, a mosaic element of volume δv is supposed to be rotated through the reflecting position with angular velocity ω, and bathed in radiation of intensity I_0 per second per unit area. The integrated energy received by the chamber is E. It can be shown that

$$E\omega/I_0 = (Ne^2|F(hkl)|^2/mc^2)^2 \cdot \lambda^3 \cdot 1/\sin 2\theta \cdot \delta v$$

$$= Q \cdot \delta v$$

It will be noted that all the factors in this formula are known, N being the number of pattern units per unit volume, e the charge on the electron, m its mass, c the velocity of light, λ the wave length, and θ the glancing angle of reflection. A measurement of E therefore leads directly to be determination of $F(hkl)$.

The fundamental point in this formula is that the integrated reflection is proportional to δv, the volume of the mosaic element, whatever its shape. This may at first sight seem surprising. If one compares two mosaic elements with the same area, but one twice the depth of the other, the reflected amplitude will be twice as great for the latter and so the intensity will be four times as great. On the other hand, the range of angle over which reflection takes place is determined by the condition that the top planes and bottom planes should not get too far out of phase, so the range is half as great for the larger element; the net result is that the integrated intensity is twice as great for the element of twice the volume, as the formula indicates.

If this proportionality did not hold, and we had to know the geography of the mosaic before assessing the efficiency of reflection, quantitative analysis would be impractical. Fortunately, as long as the mosaic elements are sufficiently small their shape does not matter, and in practice all the crystals ordinarily analysed are so 'bad' that they can be treated a ideally imperfect.

The factor Q is the basis for the formulae which apply to the various methods of measurement. If the whole crystal of volume V is so small that the X-rays are inappreciably absorbed, then the integrated reflection is $Q \cdot V$. If a beam of intensity I per second falls on the face of a crystal with absorption coefficient μ, the integrated intensity is given by $E\omega/I = Q/2\mu$. Similar expressions hold for diffraction through thin slips of crystal, or by a crystal powder.

One further factor must be taken into account, which is illustrated by Fig. 4, in Chapter 1. The scattered X-rays show polarization effects like light, and the intensity is reduced by a factor $(1+\cos^2 2\theta)/2$. For instance, when the rays are scattered through an angle of 90° ($\theta = 45°$) polarization reduces the intensity to $1/2$ (Chapter 1, section 3).

3. Extinction

Two refinements of intensity calculation may be mentioned, though in general they only concern very strong reflection from single crystals and are unimportant in the case of the highly complex structures on which analysis is now concentrated. They are known as primary extinction and secondary extinction. Primary extinction diminishes the intensity when the mosaic elements are so large that they behave as fragments of perfect crystal and so give a smaller integrated intensity. Fortunately this only holds for strong reflections, and it is on the weak reflections of higher orders that placing of atoms depends. Secondary extinction works in a different way. Mosaic elements deep down in the crystal may be robbed of their fair share of the incident beam because elements nearer the surface, which happen to have the same orientation, have weakened it. In other words, there is an apparent increase in the absorption coefficient at the Bragg angle, an effect noted by W. H. Bragg in 1913. Secondary extinction, like primary, only affects very strong reflections.

4. The Perfect Crystal

Bold spirits have set out to test the theory of diffraction by a perfect crystal with a considerable measure of success. Regions can be found in crystals of calcite which are very perfect and these have been tested. Ewald has developed the theory of the relationship between incident, refracted, and reflected waves in perfect crystals by a rigorous mathematical treatment, the 'Dynamic Theory', in a most elegant way. As far as X-ray analysis is concerned, however, these refinements are not required. The simple Darwin expression for the ideally imperfect crystal is sufficient for all needs in turning the experimental measurements into $F(hkl)$ values.

5. The Structure Amplitude $F(hkl)$

It is generally assumed that atoms are bodies with spherical symmetry, so that the waves they scatter can be treated as coming from the atomic centre. Refined measurements have to be made to detect a departure from spherical symmetry due to interatomic bonds, because it is so small. The atomic scattering factor f is equal to the number of electrons Z in the atom for zero scattering angle, and falls off as the angle increases owing to interference. It is a function of $\sin \theta/\lambda$, and so the same for a given reflection $F(hkl)$ irrespective of wavelength, because λ and $\sin \theta$ are proportional. Tables have been calculated for values of f plotted against $\sin \theta/\lambda$, and a few examples are shown in Table 1.

TABLE 1

$(\sin \theta/\lambda).$ 10^{-8}	0	0.1	0.2	0.3	0.4	0.5	0.6	0.7	0.8	0.9	1.0
0^{-2}	10.0	8.0	5.5	3.8	2.7	2.1	1.8	1.6	1.5	1.4	1.35
Na^+	10.0	9.5	8.2	6.7	5.25	5.05	3.2	2.65	2.25	1.95	1.75
Cl^-	18.0	15.2	11.5	9.3	8.05	7.25	6.5	5.75	5.05	4.4	4.1
Cu^+	28.0	27.0	24.0	20.7	17.3	14.0	11.3	9.4	8.0	7.3	7.0
Rb^+	36.0	33.6	28.7	24.6	21.4	18.9	16.7	14.6	12.8	11.2	9.9
Hg	80.0	74.9	65.9	57.8	50.3	44.6	40.3	36.9	33.5	30.5	27.8

Typical atomic scattering factors. Note the rapid falling off with angle of scattering by light atoms, as compared with a heavy atom such as mercury.

The next step is to calculate the resultant of the waves scattered by the atoms in the unit cell. A suitable origin is chosen for the coordinates x, y, z of each atom, measured parallel to the cell axes. A translation a along the a axis implies a phase difference of $2\pi h$ for the hkl reflection, hence a translation of x introduces a phase difference $2\pi hx/a$. The same is true for y and z, so an atom at (x, y, z) has a phase difference with respect to the origin of $2\pi hx/a + 2\pi ky/b + 2\pi lz/c$. Vectors with length f and with this phase are combined to form a resultant E as in Fig. 1. In such a diagram, the projection of f_1, f_2 etc. on the x axis are summed to produce OA, and those on the y axes to produce OB. F is the resultant of OA and OB, and the phase angle α is given by $\tan \alpha = OB/OA$.

6. The Wilson Criterion for a Symmetry Centre

It is convenient in this connection to consider Wilson's test for a symmetry centre, which has been mentioned in the chapter on symmetry. When a crystal has a symmetry centre and this is taken as origin, the va-

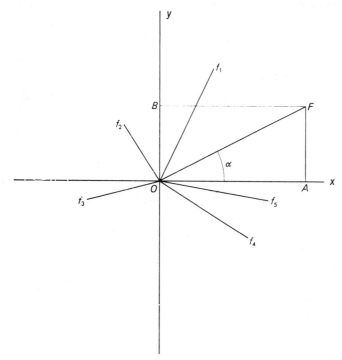

FIG. 1. Vector sum of atomic contributions f_1, f_2, f_3, f_4, f_5 to give structure factor F.

lues of $F(hkl)$ are all real, being positive or negative. This is so because the projections of the vectors on the y axis in Fig. 1 for two atoms related by the symmetry centre cancel out, leaving only the projections on the x axis. When there is no symmetry centre, there are projections of $F(hkl)$ on both axes, varying from small to large.

In the centro-symmetrical case, the resultant projection on the x axis must be small in order to give a weak reflection. In the noncentro-symmetrical case, however, it is necessary for the projections both on x and y to be simultaneously small for a weak reflection. When the one is small the other is quite likely to be large. So if the numbers of reflections are plotted statistically against their intensities, the centro-symmetrical crystal has a much larger proportion of small F values than the non-centrosymmetrical. The characteristic difference is so marked that it is a reliable criterion for symmetry centres.

For many years text-books on X-ray analysis had pronounced solemnly that the analysis was unable to detect a centre of symmetry because of Friedel's law (p. 187), until this simple relation, so obvious when pointed out, was deduced by A. J. C. Wilson.

7. Zero-Point Energy

A rigid test of the accuracy both of experimental measurement and theoretical calculation was made in 1928 by James, Waller, and Hartree. James and Waller measured the values of $F(hkl)$ with a crystal of NaCl, and so obtained experimentally the f curves for Na and Cl. A comparison of these values at different temperatures gave the Debye factor (page 38) and so they were able to extrapolate the curves to their form at absolute zero. The curves could then be compared with those calculated from Hartree's 'self-consistent field' atom models which of course were calculated for an atom at rest. It was found that the experimental curve at absolute zero still fell off faster with angle than Hartree's curve, showing the atoms were still in motion at zero temperature, and this degree of vibration proved to be consistent with the 'zero-point energy' of half a quantum predicted by quantum theory. This was the first experimental proof of the existence of zero-point energy.

8. Summary

This experiment was the culmination of a series of researches on intensity of diffraction by Bragg, James and Bosanquet in the early twenties. These researches established the validity of Darwin's equations and the accuracy of Hartree's atomic models. Rock salt, NaCl, was mainly used for these experiments; it has always been the favoured 'guinea pig' for experiments on the quantitative aspect of X-ray diffraction. They established methods for measuring values of $F(hkl)$ in all crystals. In particular, they established a reliable scale for quantitative measurement. Fundamentally, the diffracted beam must be compared with the incident beam from the X-ray tube. This is a troublesome measurement to make both because the incident beam is so extremely strong compared with the diffracted beam, and because it must be 'monochromatized' by reflection from a crystal in order that the radiation of other wave lengths may be filtered out. It is convenient to establish a standard value for some crystal and use this as a secondary standard for comparison with the crystal under investigation. The reflection 400 from rock salt is a useful standard.

To sum up, the analytical methods which have been described in this chapter show how the scattering efficiency of the unit of pattern in the crystal can be deduced from the experimental measurements. Combined with a knowledge of the space occupied by the unit of pattern and the space-group symmetry, this is the sum of the knowledge on which the X-ray analyst must base his determination of structure. It is a clean-cut process. All the results of the experimental research are summed up in a table of numbers, the F values, and these now have to be fed into whatever computing mechanism is used to work out the arrangement of the atoms which account for the tabulated F's. In the first crystal analyses reflections were only classified as strong or weak, though this sufficed for such very simple structures. The establishment of absolute values enabled X-ray analysis to be extended to far more complex crystals and opened a new chapter in its history.

CHAPTER 8

FOURIER SERIES AND TRANSFORMS

1. The Fourier Method of Analysis

The earlier methods of analysis have now been almost entirely replaced by the Fourier method, which tackles the problem of atomic arrangement from a different angle. The Fourier method is so essential for all work on complex structures that it will be described in some detail. The optical principles involved are illustrated in this chapter by a number of effects observed with visible light, and in the next chapter the ideas will be extended to X-rays and crystals. It will only be possible to deal with the essential ideas. The Fourier treatment is so important that new ways of using it continue to be found, and there is now an extensive literature on the subject; it is a surprisingly fruitful field. The basic principles, however, are simple and elegant.

2. The Fourier Series

Any periodic physical event, that is to say something which repeats at regular intervals and so can be represented by a 'periodic function', can be broken down into a series of simple wave-like forms. Notes from musical instruments provide a familiar example. Fig. 1 shows the variation in the pressure of the air for a note from (a) flute, (b) clarinet, (c) oboe, (d) saxophone. When we listen to these notes, we recognize that they may have the same pitch, but each has a quality characteristic of the instrument. This quality depends on the overtones or the accompanying harmonics which have a frequency which is a multiple of the fundamental. The note of the flute, for example, is composed almost entirely of the fundamental and the harmonic of double the frequency. The notes of other instruments are more complicated because they are richer in overtones.

The breaking down of a periodic function into a series of simple wave-forms is called 'Fourier Analysis'. Each of the wave forms is defined

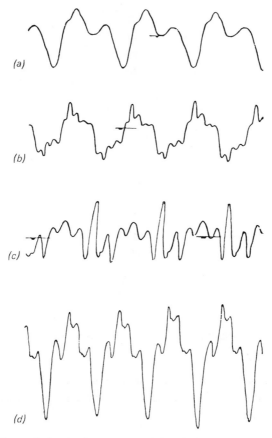

FIG. 1. The variation in the pressure of the air for a note from (*a*) flute, (*b*) clarinet, (*c*) oboe, (*d*) saxophone.

by its *amplitude* and its *phase*. The amplitude measures the strength of the harmonic, and the phase defines its position in relation to the other harmonics. Both amplitude and phase must be right in order to give a true picture of the periodic function. To return to the example of the musical notes, a close approximation to the flute note is obtained by adding together the fundamental and an overtone of twice the frequency which has an equal amplitude and is displaced by one-sixth of a period (Fig. 2(*a*)). If however these two notes are added with no displacement, the result is a quite different periodic function (Fig. 2(*b*)) although, because it contains the same combination of pure notes, it would sound the same to the ear.

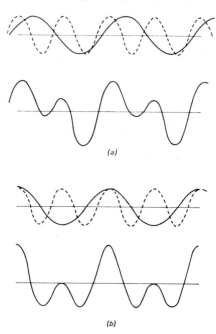

FIG. 2. Fourier synthesis of complex wave forms from harmonic components.

These wave-forms afford an example of a one-dimensional 'Fourier series'. The variation of the pressure P with time is represented mathematically by a series

$$P = P_0 + P_1 \cos(2\pi t/T - \alpha_1) + P_2 \cos(4\pi t/T - \alpha_2) + \ldots +$$
$$P_n \cos(2\pi n t/T - \alpha_n) + \ldots$$

In this formula the constant P_0 is the mean pressure of the air. The next term represents the fundamental note with amplitude P_1, the next the first overtone with amplitude P_2, and so forth. The α's are the phase angles which define the positions of the harmonic curves relatively to each other, or in other words, their relative displacement along the horizontal axis in Fig. 2.

Our ears are capable of doing a kind of Fourier analysis of a musical note. Each frequency stimulates a corresponding place in the cochlea, and the combination of these stimuli give us the impression of the quality of the note.

3. The Optical Grating as a Fourier Analyser

The principles of Fourier analysis can be applied to the formation of spectra by a transmission optical diffraction grating. The amplitude A of the light coming through the grating can be represented by a periodic function which repeats at intervals 'a', the constant of the grating (in an actual case the phase may also vary periodically, but for simplicity it will be supposed that only the amplitude varies owing to a periodic variation of the transparency). The amplitude A can therefore be represented by a Fourier series.

$$A = A_0 + A_1 \cos (2\pi x/a - \alpha_1) + \ldots + A_n \cos (2\pi nx/a - \alpha_n) + \ldots$$

just like the pressure of the air in a musical note.

When monochromatic light falls normally on such a grating, it produces spectra of zero order (the directly transmitted beam), first order, second order and so forth. It can be shown mathematically that the mth order spectrum is produced entirely by the mth order term of the Fourier series, and by that term alone. The contribution to the mth spectra from any Fourier component other than the mth always adds up to zero. Further, the amplitude of the mth order spectrum is proportional to the amplitude of the mth Fourier component. A strong 'overtone' produces a strong spectrum and vice-versa.

The mathematical proof will not be given here, because it is so easy to show that this relation holds by a simple physical example. Provided that there is no absorption, it is always possible to reverse the light in any optical arrangement. A source of light produces certain interference phenomena; if now the waves in the interference effects are made to run backwards, they will reproduce the source of light. In Fig. 3, a grating with very narrow lines is producing spectra of many orders, which proceed as plane wave trains identified in the figure by short heavy lines. If these trains are reversed in direction, and meet at the grating, they must reconstruct the distribution of light coming through the grating. How is it done? The trains of waves from each pair of spectra, right and left, produce interference fringes at the grating surface. The first order spectra produce a first order sinusoidal fringe, the second fringes twice as close and so forth. So each pair of spectra provides a Fourier component of a series which, when summed, reproduces the light coming through the grating. The grating is being 'Fourier analysed' by the spectra. The trains

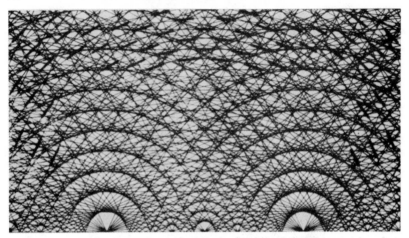

FIG. 3. Diffraction by a grating with narrow lines.

of waves at the top of Fig. 3 have been continued backwards towards the grating, and it can be seen how they are turning into the circular waves coming from the grating apertures.

4. An Optical Illustration

According to this principle a grating with only one Fourier component should give only one order of spectrum. One can make a line grating of this kind by printing out of focus from the type of process plate, ruled with about 200 lines to the inch, similar to that which is used in making half-tone printing blocks. The rulings have equal spacings of white and black at about 200 to the inch, and by exposing to a diffuse light with a slight separation between negative and print the density is not far from the form

$$A_0 + A_1 \cos 2\pi x/a.$$

There must of course be an A_0 at least equal to A_1, because the light amplitude cannot be 'negative'. If such a plate is used as an interference grating it gives a transmitted zero order, a first order on either side, and vanishingly small higher orders (Fig. 4 (*a*) and (*b*)).

On the other hand a grating with extremely narrow lines can be made by printing from the ribbed film used for certain photographic colour reproduction processes. The ribs act like cylindrical lenses and focus a light source onto the positive; the resulting narrow black lines are then

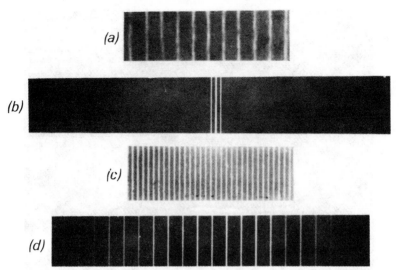

FIG. 4. (*a*) diffraction grating with simple sinusoidol variation in density and (*b*) corresponding diffraction pattern with only zero and first order spectra. (*c*) diffraction grating with many fine lines and (*d*) corresponding diffraction pattern with many high orders of spectrum.

reversed photographically into narrow transparent lines. If one looks at a sodium source through such a grating, some thirty or forty orders of spectra will be seen on either side. A Fourier series with many high terms must be used to form a grating with very narrow lines, and so there are many high orders of spectrum (Fig. 4 (*c*) and (*d*)).

5. The Cross-Grating

The same treatment can be extended to two dimensions. A cross-grating is a two-dimensional pattern, and its spectra are shown in Fig. 5. They form a two-dimensional array, in which each spot must be labelled by two indices h and k to define its order. One can see a constellation of spectra of this kind by looking at a distant light through a handkerchief or a net curtain. The holes between the threads form a two-dimensional pattern of apertures, and the light is surrounded by a galaxy of spectra.

The same principle of reversal illustrates the relationship between cross-grating pattern and the spectra. The units of a two-dimensional pattern, like for instance the regularly planted trees in an orchard, can be seen as sets of rows running in many directions. Any given set of rows produces a pair of spectra hk and $\overline{h}\overline{k}$. When the light is reversed these

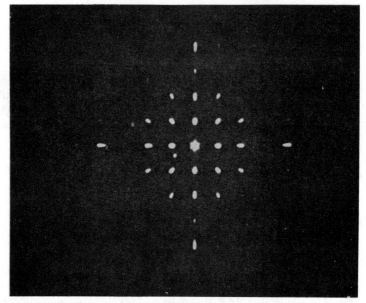

FIG. 5. Diffraction by a cross-grating.

spectra make a set of fringes, and such Fourier components criss-crossing each other in all directions reproduce the pattern as a two-dimensional Fourier series.

6. Object and Transform

Figure 6 illustrates Abbe's treatment of the formation of the image in a microscope. Monochromatic plane waves are supposed to fall on a line grating representing the object. These lines $O_1O_2O_3$ etc. produce spectra, which being parallel beams come to a focus at $S_0'S_1S_2$ etc. in the focal plane of the objective lens. The spectra may now be considered as sources of light. The waves from them form fringes; and in the image plane these fringes add together so as to reproduce the lines $O_1O_2O_3$ of the grating.

The Abbe construction illustrates what is meant by a *Transform*. The distribution of light in the image plane is a reproduction, more or less perfect, of the light coming from various points of the object. The distribution of light on the spectral plane of S_0S_1 etc. is a record of the light coming from the *whole* of the object in any given *direction*. In the simple case illustrated here the object is a grating and so the light in the spectral plane is concentrated at points. This can be generalized, however, to apply to an irregular object, in which case the transform is spread all over the spectral plane. One could in such a case use a Fourier integral instead of a Fourier series. It may be noted that this relationship is reversible. The transform of the object in Fig. 6 is in the S plane, but

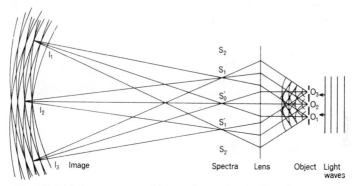

FIG. 6. Abbe's treatment of image formation in the microscope.

equally we can regard S as the object, and the original object as the transform of S. An object in the focal plane on one side of a lens gives a transform in the focal plane on the other side.

7. An Illustration of the Image-Transform Relationship. The 'Fly's Eye'

Suppose one wishes to send to a friend or relation a reminder of what one looks like. The usual method is to send a point-to-point description of the amount of light coming from various parts of one's face—in other words a photograph or portrait. The same object could be achieved, provided the recipient's powers of analysis were adequate, by sending a series of coefficients defining the phase and amplitude of light coming in various directions from one's face, in other words a transform.

These relationships are illustrated in Fig. 7. An optical device called a 'fly's eye' is used to obtain the transform. It consists of a transparent sheet on which a square pattern of minute lenses about $\frac{1}{10}$ inch apart has been formed. This is done by pressing a round point on the flat surface of a soft metal block at the points of the pattern, and then casting a plastic sheet on the block. If such a block is laid on a photographic plate and exposed to an illuminated object, each lens forms an image on the plate. The result is a cross-grating, each element of which is a reproduction of the object. This grating is then used to diffract a monochromatic beam, and the result is a series of cross grating spectra which constitute the transform.

The units of pattern in Fig. 7 (*a*) were two visages which were familiar in World War II. Repeated images of them were made by the fly's eye, and are shown much enlarged in Fig. 7(*b*). The spectra are shown diagramatically in Fig. 7(*c*); it will be noted that the transform of Stalin is more symmetrical than that of Hitler, corresponding to the greater symmetry of the object.

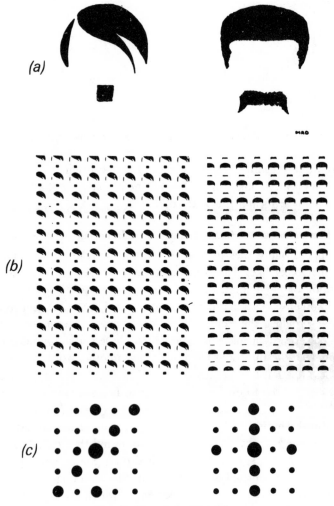

Fig. 7. Use of the Fly's Eye.

8. Focus

In Abbe's reconstruction (Fig. 6) the spectra S_0S_1 etc. are formed by parallel trains coming from the object. These parallel trains will be focused at the S points whatever the distance of the object from the objective lens, and the position and intensity of the S points will remain the same. Why then is it necessary to focus on the object?

The answer of course is that although the amplitudes remain the same the relative phases alter as the objective is racked backwards and forwards, and so the image will alter. It is only when the object is in focus that the waves from S will form a true image.

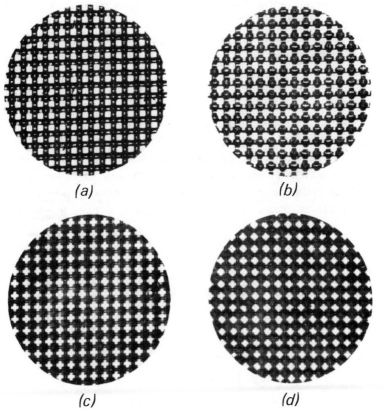

(a)   *(b)*

(c)   *(d)*

FIG. 8. (*a*) Image of a piece of wire gauze, representing a cross-grating. (*b*) (*c*) (*d*) Patterns produced from waves diffracted by gauze when the image is out of focus by various amounts.

This principle can be illustrated in an interesting way by using as an object a cross-grating pattern of transparent holes, illuminated by parallel monochromatic light. Figure 8(a) shows this pattern in focus. The many Fourier components which build it up have the right amplitudes and phases to give a simple pattern of holes. That all these components are there, 'behind the scene' so as to speak, can be shown by racking the objective lens towards or away from the object. With a small movement the higher components become first out of phase and can be seen (Fig. 8(b)) and each further movement produces a new pattern (Fig. 8 (c), (d)).

In ideal conditions the effect should not depend on the wave-length of the light. If the wave-length is shorter the spectra at S are closer together, but their fringes are still formed on the same scales. Actually this condition is not perfectly met because the lenses have small chromatic aberrations. The fringes for the different colours are not precisely superimposed, and so if one illuminates the object with parallel white light one gets a series of attractive coloured tartan patterns as the lens moves closer or further away.

9. Resolution

Abbe's construction had as its primary object the analysis of resolving power, or in other words the extent to which the image is a representation of the object, and this extent depends on how many spectra there are in the S plane. The higher terms of the Fourier series, which give detail to the image, come from the higher orders of spectra. If as in Fig. 4(b) the only spectra admitted are the zero order and first orders on

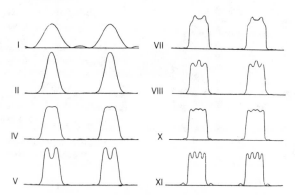

FIG. 9. Images of a grating with rectangular slits formed by various numbers of Fourier components ranging from the zero order and two first orders (I) to the zero and all pairs of orders up to the eleventh (XI) (After Porter).

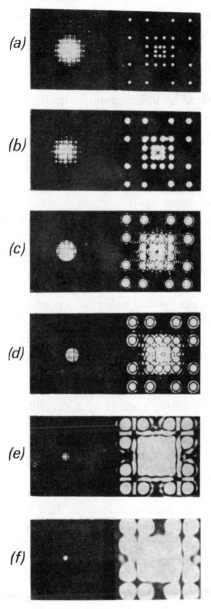

FIG. 10. Optical illustration of the relationship between resolution in an image and the extent of the diffraction pattern used in its formation.

either side, the image will be formed by a series $A_0 + A_1 \cos 2\pi x/a$, and so the lines of the grating look like simple sinusoidal distributions. If S_1 and $S_1{}'$ are cut off by a stop, or if the lines are so close that S_1, $S_1{}'$ are deviated through too large an angle to be included in the spectral plane, no lines can be seen because there are no fringes in the image plane.

Figure 9 shows a more detailed analysis of this effect by A. B. Porter. He considered an object grating with the sharp white and dark lines shown in Fig. 4(c) and he analysed this distribution into a Fourier series. By adding an increasing number of the terms of this series in formation of the image he showed that the image becomes a better representation of the object as this number increases.

The effect is shown optically by the series of photographs in Fig. 10 due to Lipson. The object was the pattern of circular holes shown in Fig. 10(a). Its transform in the S plane is the pattern on its left.

Each individual hole diffracts the light as an inner maximum surrounded by a circular halo and this effect is to be seen in the transform. A diaphragm was now placed in the transform plane S and the succeeding photographs represent the result of closing it in stages. The cutting off of the outer ring in the transform destroys information about the size of the spots, and they correspondingly become diffuse. Further reductions of the transform produce increasingly poorer reproduction, though it is remarkable that even the small amount of information in the penultimate transform tells so much about the object.

These optical examples of phase relationship and resolution have close analogies with similar features of X-ray diffraction which will be discussed in the next chapter.

10. The Deciphering of Photographs Taken with an Electron Microscope

A method of unravelling the pictures taken with an electron microscope has been developed by Klug and his colleagues. It has no direct relation to X-ray analysis, but is included here because it is such an elegant example of the image-transform relationship.

Figure 11(a) is a photograph of a tubular structure found in a form of bacteriophage. The outer coating is composed of protein molecules of molecular weight about 50,000, which are arranged in a helical fashion like a coiled spring of small pitch. The specimen has been 'negatively stained', that is to say, embedded in an electron-dense medium which fills the holes and crevices on the surface and since the protein structure in contrast is a less efficient scatterer of electrons the form of the surface is revealed. The tube is circular in cross section, but became flattened when used as an object in the microscope, so that the back and front of the helix each become a set of lines, superimposed and inclined at a small angle, as can be pictured by imagining a spring squashed flat.

Filtered images

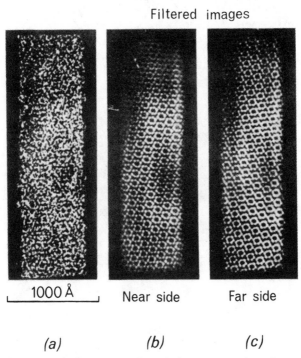

	1000 Å	Near side	Far side
	(a)	*(b)*	*(c)*

FIG. 11. (*a*) electron micrograph of a tubular structure in a form of bacteriophage. (*b*), (*c*) filtered images of the near and far sides of the same structure.

The photograph is used as subject in Fig. 12 and is illuminated with parallel monocromatic light. In order to avoid effects due to variation in thickness of the photographic film, which would introduce phase variations, it is immersed in an oil, which has the same refractive index as the film, between optical flats. The lens L_2 forms the transform shown in Fig. 13(*a*).

This transform is due to three characteristics of the subject. There is in the first place the central cross, which is the diffraction pattern due to the aperture at S through which light is admitted. Its fine structure is in fact the Fraunhofer pattern of a rectangular aperture, and has nothing to do

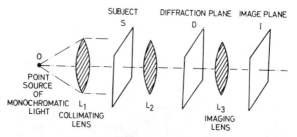

FIG. 12. Optical diffractometer.

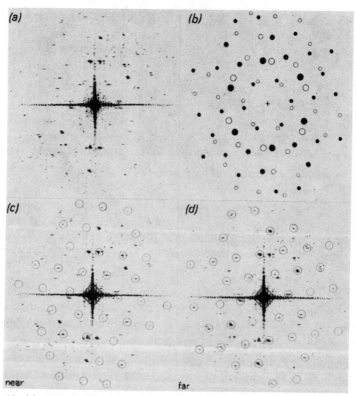

FIG. 13. (*a*) optical diffraction pattern (Fourier transform) of electron micrograph in FIG. 11. (*a*). (*b*) positions of diffraction spectra arising from long-range regularities in structure at the front and back surfaces of the object. Filtered diffraction patterns corresponding to (*c*) the front and (*d*) the back surfaces.

with the form of the object. Then there are irregular spots which represent the transform of the irregularities in the structure or uneven staining, a kind of background 'noise'. Finally, there are two sets of spots which represent diffraction by the long-range regularities in structure at the front and back respectively which are superimposed on the photograph. These are sorted out in Fig. 13(b) as black and white circles. Masks are then made with apertures which admit only the diffracted spots due to the front (Fig. 13(c)) or back (Fig. 13(d)) and these masks are placed in the diffraction plane D. The central cross must not be ignored, for if it were cut out false images would result, as they would if the constant A_0 in a Fourier series were omitted. However, only one half of the intensity in this cross is due to the front surface, the other half being due to the back surface and this is allowed for by covering the cross with a fine mesh grid which only lets one half of the light through. The pictures in the image plane which are formed when the transform is masked are shown as Fig. 11(b) (near side) and Fig. 11(c) (far side). These 'filtered' images are remarkably clear when compared with Fig. 11(a). The white objects which form rings of six are individual protein molecules separated by about 35 Å. Naturally great care must be taken in selecting a coherent set of spots in the masking, since if the wrong spots were selected false images would be produced. It must be remembered, however, that although the masking involves an element of selection, the intensities do not, and they play an important part in building up the details of the picture.

CHAPTER 9

THE FOURIER SERIES IN X-RAY ANALYSIS

1. The Fourier Principle in X-ray Diffraction

My father proposed in 1915 that the Fourier method should be applied to X-ray analysis. To quote from his Bakerian Lecture to the Royal Society:

'If we know the nature of the periodic variation of the medium we can analyse it by Fourier's method into a series of harmonic terms. The medium may be looked on as compounded of a series of harmonic media, each of which will give the medium the power of reflecting at one angle. The series of spectra which we obtain for any given set of crystal planes may be considered as indicating the existence of separate harmonic terms. We may even conceive the possibility of discovering from their relative intensities the actual distribution of the scattering centres, electrons and nucleus, in the atom.'

The extension of the Fourier method to the crystal structure is completely analogous to its application in one dimension or two dimensions as described in the last chapter. The crystal may be considered as built up of sets of strata, each set being parallel to a set of planes of the crystal lattice. If a line is drawn perpendicular to one of these sets of planes, and the density of the crystal is projected on this line, the resulting curve will be like one of those in Fig. 1, Chapter 8 representing musical notes. It can be broken down into a fundamental and overtones. The fundamental gives the Bragg reflection of the first order, and the overtones the higher orders; the strength of each reflection is proportional to the amplitude of the corresponding sinusoidal component as in an optical grating. If the amplitudes and phases of these components for all the sets of crystal planes are known, they can be added together, criss-crossing each other in all directions, and the result will be a picture of the density $\varrho(xyz)$ everywhere in the crystal.

To put this in a formal quantitative way

$$\varrho(xyz) = \frac{1}{V} \sum^h \sum^k \sum^l |F(hkl)| \cos [2\pi hx/a + 2\pi ky/b + 2\pi lz/c + \alpha(hkl)]$$

$|F(hkl)|$ is measured in electron units, and the expression after the cosine gives the sinusoidal variation at intervals in the axes of a/h, b/k, c/l and its phase α. When scaled by the factor $1/V$, where V is the volume of the unit cell, the resulting $\varrho(xyz)$ is the electron density per Å^3. The appropri-

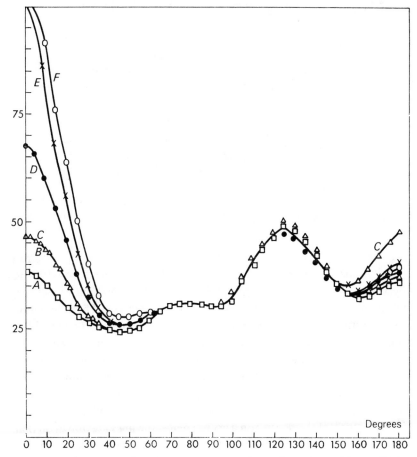

FIG. 1. Fourier summations in one, two and three dimensions. (*a*) the (111) planes in alum. (See p. 117)

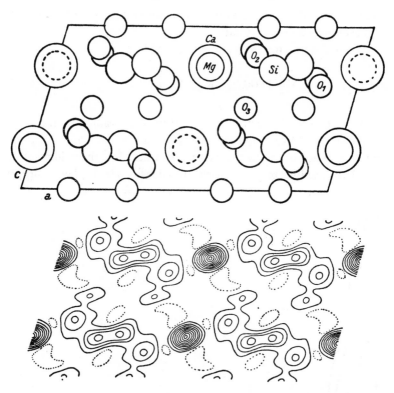

FIG. 1. (*b*) projection of the diopside structure upon (010).

ateness of the factor $1/V$ can be seen by noting that the average electron density must be $F(000)/V$. The summation is made over all positive and negative values of h, k, l. This formula is the basis of the Fourier method, which is now almost exclusively used in crystal analysis. The summation of the series gives the electron density at each point x, y, z, and the positions of the atoms are shown by peaks in the electron density, so that a plan can be made of their three-dimensional arrangement.

The information about the density is conveniently summarized by drawing contour lines through points of equal density, like the contour lines at equal heights on a map. In a simpler case when all that is needed is a projection of the density on a crystal plane, the lines are drawn on that plane. In the general case they are drawn on transparent sheets which represent sections of the unit cell, and ranges of such sheets are stacked on each other at the correct intervals so as to give a picture of the three-

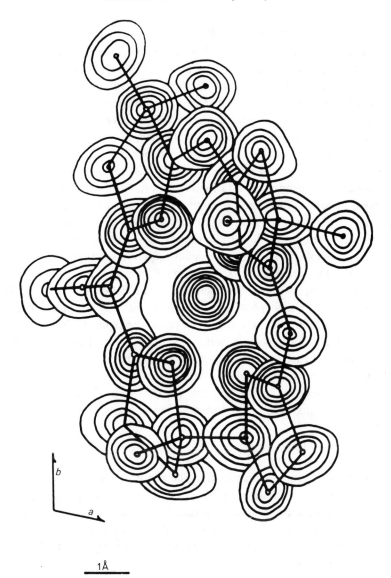

FIG. 1. (c) three-dimensional map of a part of vitamin B_{12}.

dimensional density-distribution. Figure 1 shows Fourier summations in one, two, and three dimensions and numerous other examples will be found in later chapters.

2. The Two Procedures of Analysis

The earlier method of analysis was essentially a matter of trial and error. A likely structure was assumed, and the way it would diffract X-rays was compared with experiment. If there was no correspondence, an alternative structure was tried. The comparison between calculation and observation was refined into a precise quantitative method when the laws for intensity of diffraction were established, but this did not alter the essential character of the method which depended upon being able to make good guesses at likely structures. The aids to such guesses are the knowledge of the numbers and kinds of atoms in the pattern-unit, the sizes of the atoms, their likely grouping on chemical grounds, and their fitting in with the space-group symmetry. The road to success could be much shortened by intelligent reliance on these guides, but the method centred on guessing. There was no direct road to a solution.

In the Fourier method the element of 'guessing' arises in another form. The X-ray measurements yield the *amplitudes* of the Fourier components, but not their *phases*, because they are only measurements of intensity. These intensities by themselves could be explained by an infinite number of distributions of scattering matter since the phases could have any values and each set of phases gives a different picture. The problem of analysis resolves into one of *phase determination*, and the advances which have made it possible to apply analysis to more and more complicated structures centre around new ingenious ways of finding the phases.

3. Reality

How is it ever possible to find the correct phases? The ultimate criterion is that the phases must be such as to give an acceptable physical picture. When the Fourier series is summed, it must show atoms of the right number and electron distribution, and it must give a positive density everywhere, because a negative density has no meaning. The check is one of correspondence with *reality*.

In the trial and error method this element of reality was incorporated from the start because one assumed the existence of atoms of the right number and kind. The same knowledge must now in some way be fed into the Fourier method. The position is rather like the optical problem discussed on page 97 and illustrated by Fig. 8, Chapter 8. When the illumination is monochromatic all positions of the objective give an image of some kind, but the image only reproduces the object when the phases of the Fourier series are correct. How do we know when they are correct? Because in the optical case we expect to see simple round holes, and adjust the focus till they appear. In the X-ray case we know the Fourier series must add up to show atoms, and we seek for phases which make it do so.

4. The Crystal Transform and the Reciprocal Lattice

Ewald first pointed out the advantages of considering the geometry of X-ray diffraction in terms of the *reciprocal lattice*. In this construction every set of planes (*hkl*) of the crystal is represented by a point *hkl*, which is at a distance proportional to $1/d(hkl)$ from the reciprocal origin, along a line at right angles to the planes (*hkl*). The points fixed in this way also lie on a lattice whose axes $a^*b^*c^*$ are at right angles to (100), (010), and (001) of the crystal lattice, and are in the ratio $1/d(100)$, $1/d(010)$, $1/d(001)$. The relation between a two-dimensional lattice and its reciprocal is shown in Fig. 2, and the same relation holds for three dimensions.

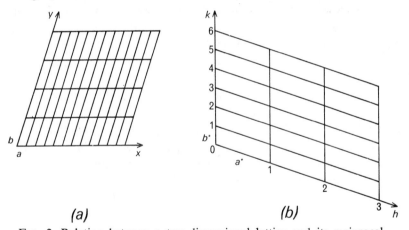

(a) *(b)*

FIG. 2. Relation between a two-dimensional lattice and its reciprocal.

The reciprocal lattice may in fact be thought of as a constellation of all the spectra which can be formed by the crystal. They cannot all be formed at the same time, as in the case of a cross-grating, because the crystal has to be in a special position for each, but analytically the principle is the same.

The analogy can be extended further. If an amplitude and phase are assigned to each of the spots, the reciprocal constellation becomes the transform of the crystal. Each point of the transform represents a period-ical term in the crystal density, as in the one-dimensional and two-dimensional cases. One gets a vivid idea of the nature of the transform from a photograph taken with the Buerger camera such as Fig. 7 (Chapter 11). The camera is designed to record all the spots in some plane of the reciprocal lattice, without a distortion of their arrangement, so the photo-graph is an accurate section.

The spots in the reciprocal lattice are ideally only precise points if the crystal is perfect and unbounded. If the crystal is of limited size or irregular, they spread into patches just as the lines in an optical spectrum become wider as the number of lines on a grating decreases. In the extreme case of no crystalline regularity, there is a continuous distribution in the transform varying in density from place to place. To sum up, all the informa-tion to reconstruct the crystal is there in the transform.

Bragg's Law in reciprocal space. The condition for reflection is shown in Fig. 3(a), where for simplicity only a two-dimensional section of the lattice is shown. The X-rays are in the direction ASO. A circle of radius $1/\lambda$ is drawn with centre at S. The reciprocal lattice has its origin at O on the circumference of this circle. If now the reciprocal lattice is turned into a position such that one of its points P lies on the circle, then

$$OP = 1/d = 2 \sin \theta / \lambda$$

where θ is the angle between the direct X-ray beam and AP.

The angle θ is therefore the glancing angle between the X-rays and the crystal planes p, which are perpendicular to OP, and the condition for reflection is satisfied because

$$\lambda = 2d \sin \theta.$$

The advantage of using the reciprocal lattice is that a set of points on a lattice is much easier to visualize than sets of crystal planes. If we picture a crystal at S turning, and the reciprocal lattice turning with it, as each point such as P falls on the circle a reflection will flash out in the direc-tion SP.

The same construction shows that in three dimensions (Fig. 3(b)) a reflection takes place when any point P falls on a sphere with centre S and radius $1/\lambda$, the sphere of reflection.

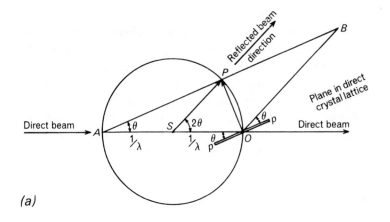

(a)

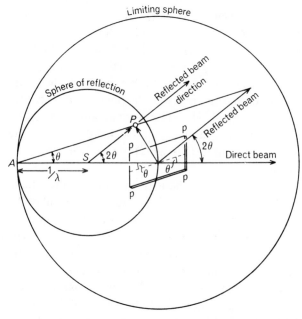

(b)

FIG. 3. The Ewald construction showing the condition for reflection in (*a*) two dimensions, and (*b*) three dimensions.

5. The Patterson Function

Before going on to illustrate the use of the Fourier method, another analytical weapon in the armoury of the X-ray analyst must be described. In a paper entitled 'A Direct Method for the Determination of the Components of Interatomic Distances in Crystals', A. L. Patterson in 1935 formulated a function which has played an extremely important part in X-ray analysis. The 'Patterson' can be formed directly from experimental measurements, there being no need to measure phases because the coefficients of its Fourier Series are proportional to intensities, not to amplitudes.

$$P = 1/V \cdot \sum\sum\sum_{\infty}^{\infty} |F(hkl)|^2 \cdot \cos 2\pi(hx/a + ky/b + lz/c)$$

When this series is summed it gives a distribution which has the following significance. If there are two points of high density (atoms) in the structure at positions x_1, y_1, z_1 and x_2, y_2, z_2 then in the Patterson synthesis there will be points of high density at $(x_1-x_2, y_1-y_2, z_1-z_2)$ and $(x_2-x_1, y_2-y_1, z_2-z_1)$. The Patterson synthesis is a map of the vectors between all pairs of atoms in the structure. It has a large maximum at the origin, because the vector between each atom and itself is zero, and these origin maxima repeat at the points of a space lattice identical with that of the crystal. The other maxima are at the ends of vectors drawn from the origin equal in magnitude and direction to the vectors between each pair of atoms, with weights proportional to the product of the weight of the atoms.

The Patterson synthesis is far more complex than the structure. If there are N atoms in the unit of pattern there will be N^2 vectors between pairs, of which N are the self-vectors which are of zero length and form the origin peak. Figure 4(a) shows an imaginary structure of identical atoms in hexagonal rings of weight S, with lighter atoms of weight O at their centres. Figure 4(b) is the corresponding Patterson synthesis which is crowded with points even in this simple case where many of the vectors coincide. It is to be noted that the weights of the points are significant as well as their positions. For instance the vector $S-S$ between nearest neighbours in the ring occurs twice, and also is equal to a vector OS, so it is represented by an exceptionally large peak.

The explanation of this significance of a Patterson synthesis is illustrated by Fig. 5. In this figure, two atoms A and B have a vector

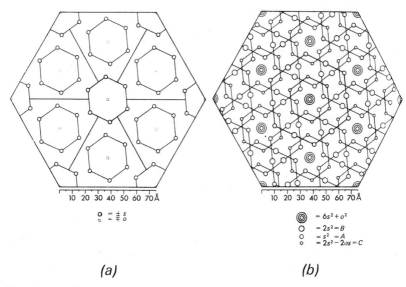

FIG. 4. Relationship between (*a*) a structure of identical atoms in hexagonal rings with lighter atoms at their centres and (*b*) the corresponding Patterson synthesis.

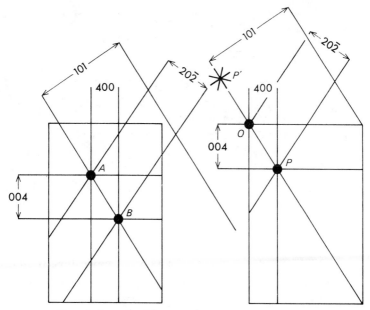

FIG. 5. Genesis of features in a Patterson synthesis.

relationship to each other such that their contributions to the 004 reflection are in phase, as shown by their lying in successive (004) planes. This also holds for successive (101) and (20$\bar{2}$) planes, as the figure shows. Therefore reflections such as 004, 101, 20$\bar{2}$ will tend to be stronger than the average, because the atoms A and B at any rate back each other up. Transferring now to the Patterson synthesis, and drawing the (004), (101), and (20$\bar{2}$) components with their maxima at the origin O, they will intersect at a point P such that OP in the Patterson synthesis is a vector equivalent to AB in the sturcture. Since they tend to have high values of F^2, there will be a maximum at P. The same will be true for the other vectors between pairs of atoms, and so the 'Patterson' is a map of vectors.

The advantage of the Patterson method is its directness, in that it requires no guessing. Its disadvantage is its complication but in spite of this difficulty it can give information of vital importance, as for instance the relative positions of heavy atoms in the structure. The Patterson

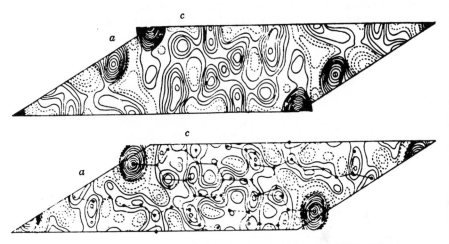

FIG. 6. Patterson projection along the *b* axis of cholesterol iodide. The heavy peaks indicate I-I vectors. Below, electron density projection calculated with terms given.

method is the first, and most famous, of a host of applications of Fourier methods, which have been specially developed because of the demands of the new science.

An example of a Patterson function is shown in Fig. 6.

6. Centro-symmetrical Structures

The problem of phase determination is greatly simplified when the pattern has symmetry centres or, in the case of a projection, axes which are equivalent to symmetry centres. Such a centre governs all properties of the crystal, so that any Fourier term in the density distribution must of necessity have either a maximum or a minimum at a centre of symmetry, which is conveniently chosen to be an origin of reference. The phase must be O or π, or to put it in another way, $F(hkl)$ must be either plus or minus. In the absence of such centres the phase can have any value.

The advantage of this simplification is that a quite rough approximation to the true structure is often sufficient to decide between the alternatives $+$ or $-$, especially in the case of the strong reflections which are the most important. It is not necessary to know the exact positions of the atoms in making this choice. A guess at the structure which is approximately right makes it possible to form a Fourier series in which a large number of terms have the correct signs. This series indicates more accurate positions of the atoms, which can then be used to decide the signs of weaker or higher order terms which were previously uncertain, and perhaps to correct others. Once one has started on the right path a few stages of refinement lead to an accurate structure determination.

The Fourier method used in this way has a very great advantage when the structure is complex with many atoms in the unit cell. In the 'trial and error' method, it becomes very tedious to test adjustments of many atomic positions when seeking the best agreement between calculation and observation; it becomes impossible to do so when the number of atoms runs into double figures. The Fourier method, on the other hand, refines the positions of all the atoms simultaneously. There is no need to deal with them individually, and structures with a hundred or more atoms can be analysed.

An instance of the efficiency of the method is shown in Fig. 7. Hydrogen atoms have a very low scattering power and it would hardly be practicable to fix their position by seeking a best fit. On the other hand, by determining the signs of F's from the positions of the heavier atoms in the molecule, and forming a Fourier series, the hydrogen positions show up clearly provided the F values have been accurately determined.

The advent of the Fourier method used in this way opened a new chapter in analysis because it made it possible for the first time to cope

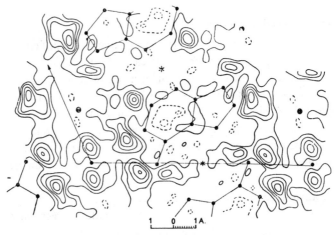

F<small>IG</small>. 7. Difference electron density map showing the positions of hydrogen atoms in the structure of adenine hydrochloride.

with organic molecules with their many atoms and low symmetry. At first only structures which were centro-symmetrical were tackled, because general phases presented far more formidable problems. The element of guessing a likely structure as a starting point was still there—what the Fourier method provided was a rapid way of refining a structure in cases where the older method could have been very tedious if not impossible.

7. The Use of the Heavy Atom. 'Staining' the Molecule

Practically all investigations of complex structures now depend on the employment of 'Heavy Atom' methods. The main constituents of such structures are carbon, nitrogen, oxygen, and hydrogen atoms in their hundreds. There is no outstanding feature in such molecules. They have a uniform conglomeration of light atoms and there is nothing to 'catch on to' in making a start on the analysis.

Fortunately, however, it is nearly always possible to add one or more heavy atoms to such a molecule, for instance a complex containing mercury, or an iodine atom. The positions of these heavy atoms in the unit cell are generally easy to determine. In a Patterson synthesis the vectors between two heavy atoms stand out strongly amongst the far weaker vectors due to the light atoms, since their weight is proportional to the products of the masses, and it is easy to interpret these vectors in terms of atomic position because they are few in number. When the heavy atom positions are fixed, various devices can be used to relate the positions of the lighter atoms to them. It is rather like the common process in microscopy of staining the specimen to reveal its structure.

There are two main ways of using the heavy atom. The first and most direct way is available when the atom enters into the structure isomorphously, or replaces a lighter atom isomorphously, so that the rest of the crystal structure remains unchanged. The second and less direct method must be used when, although a heavy atom can be attached to the molecule without changing the molecular structure, the crystal assemblage is changed; in other words, isomorphous substitution is not possible.

8. Isomorphous Substitution or Addition of a Heavy Atom

In the method now to be described the element of 'guessing' is by-passed, and the structure is determined directly. This directness has made it possible to extend X-ray analysis to far more complex bodies, largely because a regular procedure for analysis can be laid down and orders to carry it out can be programmed for a computer.

An early instance in which isomorphous substitution was used is illustrated in Fig. 1(a). The alums have the formula $R^+R^{3+}(SO_4)_2$. 12 H_2O where R^+ may be ammonium, potassium, rubidium, caesium, or thallium and R^{3+} may be aluminium, chromium, or iron. The monovalent and trivalent cations in the cubic crystals are arranged like the sodium and chlorine ions in NaCl, at alternate corners of cubes. Since the structures are centrosymmetrical the values of F are positive or negative and a measurement of the F values for different alums provides a wealth of information for determining the signs.

If an R^+ atom is taken to be at the origin, and the substitution of a heavier for a lighter atom at this point increases the absolute value of $F(hkl)$, then $F(hkl)$ must be positive; if F is decreased by the substitution it must be negative. Cork determined the signs of the $F(hkl)$'s in this way and combined them as a linear series which gives the density-distribution in sheets parallel to the (111) plane of the crystal. The curves in Fig. 1(a) represent the results for

A (NH$_4$) Al(SO$_4$)$_2$. 12 H$_2$O
B KAl(SO$_4$)$_2$.   12 H$_2$O
C KCr(SO$_4$)$_2$.   12 H$_2$O
D RbAl(SO$_4$)$_2$.   12 H$_2$O
E CsAl(SO$_4$)$_2$.   12 H$_2$O
F TlAl(SO$_4$)$_2$.   12 H$_2$O

The peak on the left represents the R^+ cation, that on the right the R^{3+} cation, and the distribution between is due to the SO_4 groups and water. The curves coincide on the right except for C where Cr replaces Al. They increase in height on the left as the atomic weight increases, B and C coincide on the left because they both represent K^+.

The above example was a very simple case. The first application of this principle to a two dimensional projection which demonstrated its great power, was made by J. M. Robertson in 1935 in the solution of the structure of phthalocyanine $C_{32}N_8H_{18}$. There are two centro-symmetrical molecules per unit cell in the crystal and the figures refer to the projections of these molecules on the 'b' plane of the monoclinic structure. The molecules are planar, and slanted so as to make an angle of about 45° with the plane of projection so that they are foreshortened laterally in Fig. 8; the outer rings are actually hexagons. The centre of the molecule is on a centre of symmetry, and the essential point is that a nickel atom can be placed here without disturbing the structure; the conditions are ideal for the isomorphous replacement method.

It might be thought that one nickel atom, of atomic number 28, would hardly alter appreciably the F value due to 32 carbon atoms of atomic number 6 and 8 nitrogen atoms of atomic number 7 (neglecting hydrogen), when $32 \times 6 + 8 \times 7 = 234$. The average alteration is quite appreciable because the contribution of the nickel atom at a symmetry centre has its full F value, whereas the contributions of the carbon and nitrogen atoms are weakened by their wide distribution of phase relationships. The result is like that of the 'Drunkard's Walk'. The drunkard, starting from a point A, makes n sorties of length l, with a random change in direction between each sortie, and arrives at a point B. On the average what distance AB has he gone? The answer is $l\sqrt{n}$. when the sober man would have gone a distance nl. In the X-ray case, the contributions of the light atoms are summed vectorially, and owing to the wide range of their phases the average result of n atoms each contributing f, is $\sqrt{n} \cdot f$. The average of the F values for the 40 atoms of carbon and nitrogen starts at $\sqrt{40} \cdot 6 = 38$ and falls off rapidly whereas the contribution of the nickel atom, has a maximum value of 28 and falls off slowly with increasing angle. The nickel contribution is therefore comparable with that of all the other atoms and in fact makes most of the F values positive. This feature, which applies also to far larger molecules, is all-important in the heavy atom substitution method.

A comparison of the F values for the metal-free compound and the

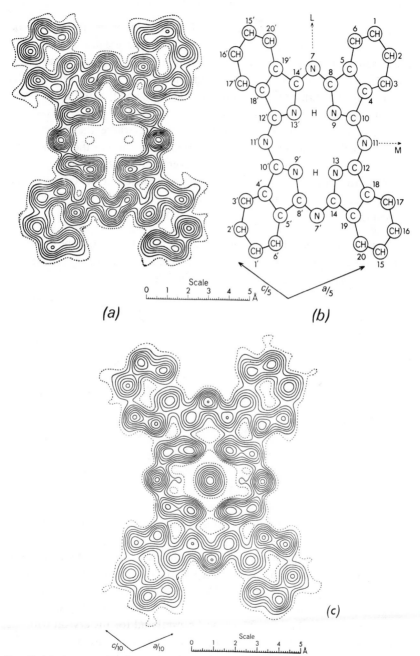

FIG. 8. (a) electron density map of phthalocyanine with (b) key and (c) corresponding map of nickel phthalocyanine.

nickel compound enables the sign of each Fourier component to be fixed, as in the simple case of the alums. If F is greater in the nickel compound, it must be positive, if less it must be negative. The result of summing the series with the F values for the metal-free compound is shown in Fig. 8(*a*), its interpretation in Fig. 8(*b*), and the Fourier diagram for the nickel compound in Fig. 8(*c*).

It might be thought that this was a case where the structure is determined without any assumptions about the nature of the units which are scattering the X-rays. This is, however, not so. It is assumed that a nickel atom, of known scattering power, is situated at the centre of the molecule, and this assumption provides the link with 'reality' which is essential to all X-ray analysis.

Phase Determination in the General Case. This principle may be extended to phase determination where there is no centre of symmetry and for all values of h, k, l. Figure 9 shows the principle.

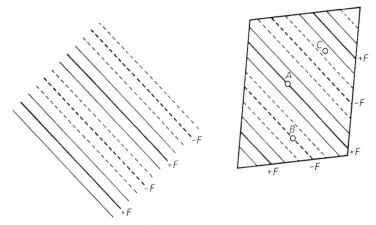

FIG. 9. The method of isomorphous replacement.

There are various ways of finding the positions of heavy atoms in the unit cell although the rest of the structure is unknown and it will be assumed that this has been done. Heavy atoms such as A, B, C have been added isomorphously at different known points, and in each case measurements of the F values for the natural crystal and for the crystal with the heavy-atom additive have been compared. The orientation of a Fourier component of density is indicated by the continuous and dotted lines, but its phase, that is to say its position relatively to the unit cell, has to be found. If adding A increases $|F(hkl)|$ then we know that a positive crest of the Fourier component must include A. If there is a decrease for B, B must lie in a trough of the Fourier component. If C makes little difference, its contribution must be about $90°$ out of phase. By such considerations the position of the Fourier component in the unit cell can be pinned down. The determination can be made quantitative by drawing vector diagrams as in Fig. 10(b). Since the position of A with respect to the origin is known, the amplitude and phase of its contribution to the scattering can be represented by the vector 00_A in the figure. The absolute value of the *amplitude* $|F|$ of the scattering due to the molecule is known, but not its phase, so the end of the vector representing it may lie at any point on the circle with radius $|F|$ and O as centre. The *amplitude* $|F_A|$ for the molecule plus heavy atom A is now measured, and it is known that the resultant of f_A and F must be F_A. In other words, the triangle f_A, F, F_A must close. If a circle is drawn with O_A as centre and radius F_A and if this cuts the first circle at a point P, the triangle $OO_A P$ will satisfy this condition. OP is therefore a possible vector for the molecule as regards both phase and amplitude.

It is not the only possibility, because the answer might be the vector OQ where the circles also cut. If, however, a second heavy atom substitution can be made at another place B, and the same construction is followed (see Figure) there will in general be only one place where the three circles cut, so that the vector OP is decided without ambiguity.

Figure 10(b) shows actual examples of the use of this method in protein analysis. The heavy circle in each case has a radius equal to the amplitude for the protein molecule without additive, and the light circles are drawn as in Fig. 10(a) for five different kinds of heavy atom additive. The circles do not intersect precisely at a point owing to experimental error, but the phase is very definitely indicated in each case.

Such a method can only be used when the crystalline forms are isomorphous. The addition of the heavy atoms must not change the form of the molecule in any way, since otherwise the construction shown in Fig. 10(a) would be meaningless, because the difference between F and F_A would be due to shifts of atomic position as well as to the addition of the heavy atom. Up till now, it is only the proteins which have satisfied this condition. The molecules are so enormous that they can accommodate the addition of a heavy atom or a complex containing a heavy atom without distortion; smaller molecules are distorted too much for the method to work.

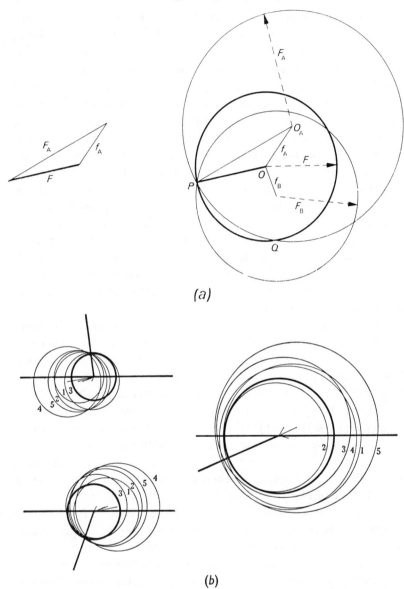

(a)

(b)

FIG. 10 (*a*) phase determination by the method of multiple isomorphous replacement. (*b*) examples of phase determination. The heavy circle represents the amplitude of the reflection from unsubstituted protein and the light circles the amplitudes reflected from five derivatives. The short lines from the centres are the heavy-atom vectors; the heavy line indicates the phase angle eventually selected.

The method also depends on very accurate measurements of F values since the alterations produced by the heavy atom are often relatively small.

Determination of the Position of the Heavy Atom. A direct method is available in case of isomorphous replacement called the 'Difference Patterson'. Considering centro-symmetrical structures or projections in the first place, the values of $|F|$ for the natural crystal and $|F_A|$ for the crystal with the derivative are known. Whatever their signs, $|F_A| - |F|$ will be equal to $|f_A|$ due to the heavy atom. A Patterson synthesis formed

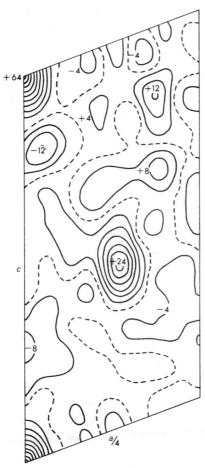

FIG. 11. Difference Patterson synthesis for a heavy-atom derivative of haemoglobin.

with coefficients $|f_A|^2$ will therefore give a Patterson map corresponding to the heavy atoms alone; the rest of the crystal will be dissolved away, so to speak, leaving them to stand out. This is useful in cases when the peaks between the heavy atoms, though relatively so strong, are not decipherable amongst the great mass of peaks due to the many lighter atoms.

The first occasion on which this method was used by Perutz is a good example of its use. He was examining a projection of the haemoglobin crystal on the (010) plane. As there is a twofold axis perpendicular to this plane, the projection is centro-symmetrical. He had found it possible to attach a complex para-chloromercuribenzoate to the molecule in an isomorphous way, and measured the consequent changes in values of $|F(hol)|$. The resulting difference Patterson function is shown in Fig. 11.

As the molecules are situated on the twofold axes of symmetry, the mercury groups are attached at two points in each molecule on opposite sides of the axis. The main vector is that between this pair of mercury atoms. Although there are irregularities in the Patterson map due to errors of measurement, this main vector is represented quite definitely by a large maximum. The vector has components of $0.136a$, $0.58c$ so the coordinates of the mercury position must be

$$x = 0.068a$$

$$z = 0.29c$$

The relationship is not true when there are no centres of symmetry. There may be little difference between $|F_A|$, and $|F|$, owing to the vector f_A being nearly at right angles to F. However, in that obliging way characteristic of Fourier series, although the method is not sound it works! On the whole f_A values which are large will give large alterations of F, and though incomplete the Patterson function still indicates the heavy atom positions, and enables the methods based on them to be applied.

9. General Employment of Heavy-Atom Methods

In the majority of cases isomorphous replacement is not possible. Heavy atoms or complexes containing them can be attached to the molecule, but they entirely alter the way the molecules pack into crystals, so the comparison of diffraction with and without a heavy-atom attachment is not available. A number of elegant methods of analysis have been developed which are based on the presence of a heavy atom amongst a large number of light atoms.

There are three kinds of peak in the Patterson diagram. The vectors between the heavy atoms are the most prominent and can be used to find the positions of these atoms in the unit cell. There will be thousands of vectors between the C, N, and O atoms which will form an undecipherable image of small peaks. An intermediate set are the vectors between the heavy atoms and the light ones, and if the structure is not too complex it may be possible to sort these out and use them. If a set of such vectors is transferred from the Patterson origin to a known heavy atom position, their ends will then lie on the actual positions of the atoms in the unit cell. Repeating this process for other known heavy atom positions should bring further peaks into coincidence with the first set and thus make it possible to select those which are significant, so that the form of the molecule takes shape.

Another device which can be used is to assume that the phases are determined by the heavy atoms alone, and to form a Fourier synthesis with these phases. This is of course not accurate, but because the influence of the heavy atoms in fixing the phase is so great, there is quite a measure of similarity between the phases calculated in this way and the true phases. Such a synthesis often outlines the relative positions of the light atoms in the immediate neighbourhood of the heavy atom. These atoms can then be used to improve the phases and a new Fourier synthesis formed, which in its turn gives more phases, and so the structure comes into focus by stages. The first application of this principle to a two-dimensional projection was made by Beevers and Lipson who worked out the structure of copper sulphate pentahydrate. They made the measurement in my laboratory on the ionisation spectrometer (p. 31) and used the copper and sulphur as the heavy atoms. More recently, the process of building outwards from a crucial heavy atom was used dramatically in the famous solution by Dorothy Hodgkin of vitamin B_{12}, which has a cobalt atom at the centre of the molecule.

These are merely examples of the many ways in which Fourier series may be used. It is a very flexible analytical tool. The process is only possible because the calculations of the many stages of refinement can be done so rapidly by the computer. Indeed, as described in the chapter on Organic Compounds, in many cases the whole process can be carried out by programming the computer and the structures of organic molecules churned out by feeding the measurements into the instrument, which produces a map of the molecule without human intervention!

10. Resolution

The principles governing the resolution of Fourier representation in X-ray analysis are the same as those described in the last chapter. The greater the number of Fourier elements of high order which are incorporated in the summation, the closer will be the correspondence between image and object.

The limits of resolution are shown in an instructive quantitative way in Fig. 12, due to N. E. White. Fourier components have been used in Fig. 12(a) which are obtained from all planes with spacings greater than 0.77 Å, and as will be seen the atoms of a pyrimidine ring attached to a chlorine atom stand out clearly. The series is terminated at spacings of

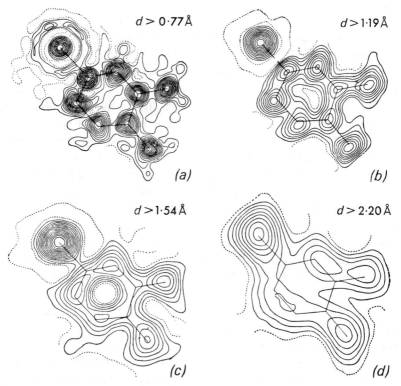

FIG. 12. Electron density projections for 4 : 5-diamino-2-chlorpyrimidine using different numbers of reflections. The measured structure factors have been modified to correspond with those from atoms at rest and the numbers used cut off at the spacings shown. Hence the patterns, particularly (a), show marked diffraction effects, as well as the effect of the termination of the series.

1.19 Å, 1.54 Å, and 2.20 Å in the following figures, and the resolution is correspondingly reduced.

The X-ray wavelength is one factor which limits resolution. As θ approaches 90°, the spacing d approaches $\lambda/2$. Since the wavelength of CuKα is 1.54 Å, for instance, a termination at a spacing of 0.77 Å as in Fig. 12(a) is as far as one can go. Such a limit is in practice sufficient to separate atoms clearly, and is a reason why Cu radiation is so useful. The Fourier series may also be limited by the state of the crystal. Temperature causes vibrations of the atoms which weaken the higher orders (Chapter 3) and imperfect crystallization has the same effect. In the protein crystals, for instance, reflections corresponding to spacings less than 2 Å in general become very weak, and the Fourier series must be terminated at this point. The representation of atomic position therefore resembles that in Fig. 12(c) and (d), and must be interpreted with the help of independent knowledge of molecular form. The lack of definition in such a case is not due to insufficient terms being measured; the Fourier series is giving a true picture of the 'fuzziness' of the molecular arrangement.

The diffraction effects mentioned in the legend of Fig. 12 are shown by the ring of density around the chlorine atom. This is of course an artefact due to the termination of the Fourier series at a point where the $|F|$ values are still appreciable. It would disappear if higher orders of $|F|$ were included.

To sum up, the rule that it becomes impossible to resolve two objects if they are closer together than half a wavelength applies to X-rays just as it does to visible light.

Note: The source for Figure 7 on p. 116 is Cochran, W. (1951) *Acta. Cryst.* 4, 81.

CHAPTER 10

OPTICAL METHODS IN X-RAY ANALYSIS

1. Optical Computing Methods

The analogy between the diffraction of X-rays and the diffraction of light has been applied to devising ways of using optical methods for analysing structures. These ways are in effect analogue computers, in which the calculations are made by the interference of light waves. Although their use has been limited, they have been effective in certain cases, as for instance in the solution of the penicillin structure. These and other calculating devices for aid in analysis have however been almost entirely superseded now that rapid digital computers are available which make calculations more accurately. Nevertheless, they will be described briefly here, because they are good examples of diffraction principles.

There are two types of optical device, corresponding to the Fourier methods of analysis and to the earlier 'trial and error' method, both of which depend on the relation between image and transform. In Abbe's treatment of image formation in the microscope, illustrated in Fig. 6, Chapter 8, the transform of the object $O_1O_2O_3$ is formed as spectra $S_1S_2S_3$. Conversely the light from these spectra, considered as object, would form the transform $O_1O_2O_3$ if the light were reversed. The relationship object–transform is reciprocal. In each case the parallel light coming from the whole of one picture is concentrated at a point in the other and vice versa.

The optical methods only apply to two-dimensional projections of the crystal structure by making use of the analogy between spectra produced by a cross-grating and X-ray reflections around a zone. The first form of device employs the measured spectra as sources of light to form an image of the projected atomic arrangement. The second type starts with a representation of a guessed atomic arrangement and produces a set of spectra which can be compared with the observed spectra.

The author together with H. Lipson first explored these devices in 1939. Further developments have largely been due to Lipson and Taylor and are described in their book on *Optical Transforms*.

2. Conversion of Transform into Object

The scheme of the apparatus is shown in Fig. 1. Light from a monochromatic source (a mercury lamp with a filter) at L passes through a pinhole F. The lens A converts the light into a parallel beam. It passes through a mask G in which holes are cut whose area are proportional to the amplitude of the F values. G is at the principal focus of the lens B, and the waves from these 'spectra' interfere in the plane S to form an image of the atomic arrangement, S being at the focus of B on the opposite side.

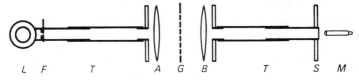

$$L \quad F \quad\quad T \quad\quad\quad A \;\; G \;\; B \quad\quad T \quad\quad S \quad M$$

FIG. 1. The optical diffractometer.

An example is shown in Fig. 2. In the projection of the diopside structure on (010) the calcium and magnesium atoms are superimposed, and their combined weight is so great that if the origin is chosen at that point, all phases referred to it are positive. (This point is discussed earlier on page 118.) A mask was made with holes proportional in area to the $|F|$ values, the holes being arranged in the position of the reciprocal lattice (Fig. 2(a)).

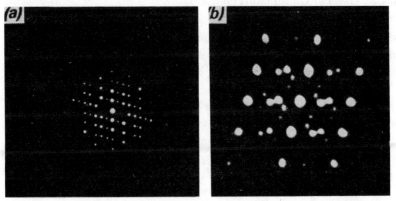

FIG. 2. Optical synthesis of an image of the structure of diopside.

Each pair of holes on either side of the origin thus produces its corresponding set of fringes with correct amplitude and spacing in the image plane *S*, and these fringes will combine to form an image of the crystal structure. That they actually do so, in a rather imperfect way, is shown by Fig. 2(*b*) which may be compared with Fig. 1(*b*), Chapter 9. The correspondence is only close in the middle of the image because of diffraction effects. The scattering by the large holes representing the stronger spectra falls off more rapidly with increasing angle than that from the small holes, hence the proportionality between *F* and amplitude of light only holds near the middle.

This device was termed the 'X-ray microscope', because it shows what one would actually see if the diffracted beams could be focused and viewed through an objective. It is not a practical device. The diopside (010) projection described above is a special case when all the *F* values are positive whereas in general, in a centro-symmetrical crystal, they are positive and negative. Ways have been devised for altering the path length for light coming through the 'negative' holes by half a wavelength, which alters their phase by 180°. Buerger, for instance, used tilted thin mica sheets placed as required over holes representing negative values of *F*. Lipson and Taylor describe other devices. It would be possible to extend them to cases needing general phase-changes. But it is much simpler, in practice, to use a computing machine which is fed with the information about phases and amplitudes and calculates the density distribution. The optical device is only described here because the principle of it is interesting.

3. Conversion of Object into Transform

This process, which corresponds to guessing a structure and testing whether it explains the spectra, is much simpler because no phase difficulties come in, and it is a more practical proposition which has been of real service in X-ray analysis.

One way of doing this conversion is to use the 'Fly's Eye' described on page 95. A model is made of the crystal structure in the unit cell projected onto a plane, the atoms being represented by holes cut in the mask. This mask is illuminated from behind, and the lenses of the fly's eye produce images of it on a photographic plate forming a cross grating with a molecule at each lattice point. The grating is illuminated by parallel monochromatic light and the spectra compared with the observed intensities.

Two difficulties have to be overcome. If there are atoms of different scattering power in the crystal they can be represented by holes of different size in the mask with areas corresponding to the scattering power. As in the previous case, however, the scattering from a large hole falls off with increasing angle more quickly by diffraction than the scattering from a small hole, which is just the wrong way round because the X-ray scattering of a heavy atom falls off more slowly with angle than that by a light atom (Chapter 7). There will therefore be serious errors in the intensities of the higher orders. Further, crystals differ in their axial ratios and interaxial angles, so ideally a suitable fly's eye ought to be made for each case; this would be too laborious.

These difficulties have been met in the ingenious way illustrated in Fig. 3. It again refers to the (010) projection of diopside (this crystal was a kind of 'fruit-fly' for many early diffraction methods). The rhomb of the unit cell has been transformed into a square, and the positions and shape of the atoms are changed to correspond. In order to make the scattering by the oxygen atoms fall off more rapidly with angle, they are represented by thin ellipses. The silicon atoms are thicker ellipses, and the superimposed calcium and magnesium atoms are solid. Fig. 3(*a*) shows a portion of the fly's eye cross-grating, and Fig. 3(*b*) shows the spectra it produces which agree very well with the observed *F* values.

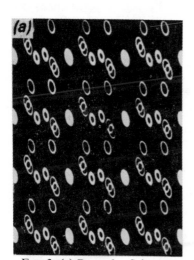 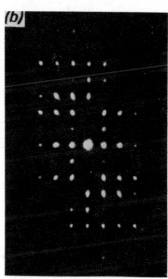

FIG. 3. (*a*) Part of a fly's eye cross-grating of the diopside structure with (*b*) its diffraction pattern.

4. Transforms of Single Molecules

It is not necessary to use the fly's eye when checking the correspondence between calculated and observed results. It can be done by matching the observed spectra against the transform of a single unit of pattern. This method has been developed by Lipson and he designed for it a more sophisticated form of diffractometer for producing the transform of an object, which is shown in Fig. 4. S_0 is the monochromatic source, a

FIG. 4. Design of improved optical diffractometer.

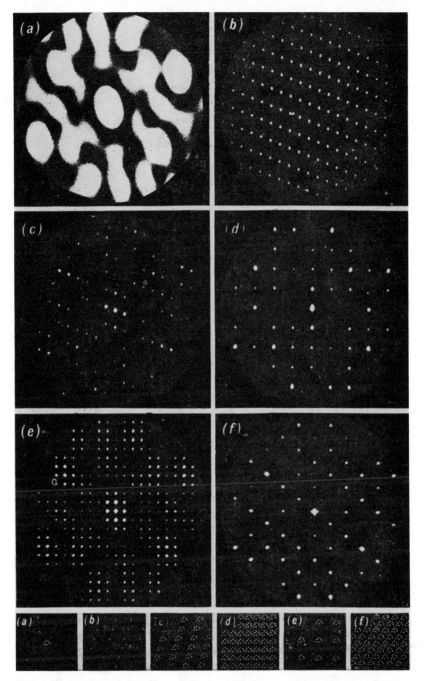

FIG. 5. Illustration of the effect of the size of unit cell. (a) is the transform of a single unit, (b) of a lattice of holes, and (c) of the convolution of the two. (d), (e) and (f) are transforms of convolutions with lattices of different forms. Scales: Transforms $\times 50$. Masks $\times \frac{1}{4}$; portions only of the masks are shown for (b), (c), (d), (e) and (f).

mercury lamp with a filter. The light passes through a pinhole at S_1. The lens L_1 makes it parallel, and the lens L_2 focuses it at F when the pattern can be observed or photographed. For convenience of viewing, the light is reflected at the mirror M. The lens L_1 and L_2 must be of good quality, because any local flaws or other defects seriously upset the interference pattern.

A mask in which holes have been cut to represent the proposed arrangement is placed between L_1 and L_2, and its transform is formed at F. A 'weighted reciprocal lattice' is prepared to the same scale as the transform. The intensities of the diffracted spots are represented on the corresponding points of the lattice by black dots of corresponding area. This weighted reciprocal lattice is superimposed on the transform. If the structure has been guessed correctly the large dots should fall on places where the transform has a high value because these correspond to directions of strong scattering by the unit of pattern.

Figure 5 shows examples from *Optical Transforms* by Taylor and Lipson. For a correct structure the strong reciprocal lattice spots fall in places where the transform has a high value and the spots are weak or absent when the value of the transform is low. Incorrect structures give markedly less good agreement.

Since alternative versions of the pattern can be rapidly prepared as masks, this optical method provides a ready way of checking whether a postulated structure is on the right lines.

Recognition of molecular orientation. An elegant example of the ready recognition of the orientation of a planar molecule is shown in Fig. 6. The transform depends on a summation $\Sigma f \cos 2\pi(hx/a + ky/b + lz/c)$. If the x and y axes are taken in the plane of a planar molecule, z is zero, and so the transform at any point depends on x and y alone. Consequently the transform is a series of spikes perpendicular to the plane of the molecule. These spikes would be rods of constant density for point atoms, but since the f values fall with increasing angle the spikes decrease in density as the distance from the central plane of the transform increases.

The figure shows the three dimensional weighted reciprocal lattice of naphthalene, formed by stacking two-dimensional weighted sections of the lattice on top of each other. The transform of a benzene ring has as its most marked feature six maxima arranged in a hexagon around the central maximum. Similar maxima occur in the transform of naphthalene, since it is two united benzene rings in a plane. If the weighted re-

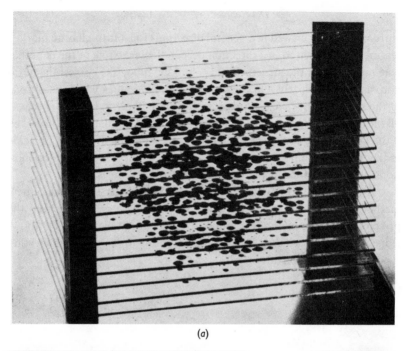

(a)

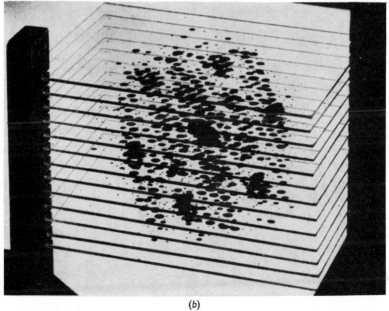

(b)

FIG. 6. The three-dimensional weighted reciprocal lattice of napthalene viewed (a) in a general direction, and (b) perpendicular to one of the molecules in the structure.

ciprocal lattice is viewed in a general direction (Fig. 6(*a*)) it has no marked features, but if viewed in a direction perpendicular to one of the naphthalene molecules in the structure one is looking along the spikes, the hexagon stands out clearly. On the average, the *hkl* values which lie on one of the spikes of the benzene ring transform are likely to be large, because all the atoms of the ring scatter X-rays in phase. A similar ring is observed if the model is viewed perpendicularly to the other naphthalene molecule in the unit pattern. It is therefore possible to deduce directly the orientations and dimensions of the two naphthalene molecules.

Although the computer has to a large extent superseded such optical methods of analysis, it has not done so entirely. It is well to keep the principles of these methods in mind, because from time to time a knowledge of them provides a lead to the solution of some new interesting type of diffraction picture.

CHAPTER 11

METHODS OF MEASUREMENT

1. The Two Main Types of Measuring Apparatus

Experimental methods of measurement determine the intensities of a range of diffracted beams, and these are then converted into absolute values of $|F(hkl)|$ which form the basis for determining the crystal structure.

In the early days, methods of measurement were relatively simple, but they have now become so sophisticated and complex that only a brief description of them can be given here. There have always been two main ways of measuring, either by recording the beams on a photographic plate, or recording them by some electrical device such as an ionization chamber or Geiger counter. It is interesting to note how first the one, then the other, has been the most widely used method. The advantage of the photograph is that it records a large number of *hkl* spectra on the same plate or film, but it does not lend itself easily to accurate quantitative measurement. The main advantage of the ionization chamber or its equivalent is that the measurement of the integrated intensity is straightforward and accurate. On the other hand it has the disadvantage that the spectra must be laboriously measured one by one.

X-ray analysis started with the Laue photograph. Although this method was developed further by Wyckoff in America, with a considerable measure of success, it never came into general use. It is too hard to attach a quantitative significance to the intensity of the spots, which are due to the superposition of diffracted beams of several orders selected from a range of 'white' radiation. The spectrometer proved to be of much greater analytical power because it measured accurately a diffracted beam of monochromatic radiation of definite order, and the first crystal structures were solved by it. It was not widely adopted in other laboratories, however, and photographic methods came to the fore again. It was becoming necessary to measure a large number of diffracted beams as analysis was extended to more complex crystals, and investigators had not the patience to deal with them one by one. I suspect a further reason was a general reluctance to use the ionization chamber which required expert handling. There were not many laboratories with experience in its use, such as my father had, whereas a photograph presented no difficulties. Various photographic methods were devised, together with new methods of 'densitometry' for measuring the blackening of the films.

Then there was a swing of the pendulum back towards ionization methods. The advent of advanced electronic devices, and of the computer, removed the tedium of laborious examination of the spectra one by one. A machine could be given orders to set the crystal and measuring chamber at the right angles for one spectrum after another and to record the results.

At the present time (1971) it would seem that once more the photographic method is going to replace ionization methods in dealing with crystals which have very large unit cells, and so produce a very large number of diffracted beams. Densitometry has been brought to such a fine art that it comes well within the range of desired accuracy, and it can be automated so that a machine scans the photograph and records the intensities.

The accuracy to be aimed at is in the region of 2% to 4% in intensity. It is a fortunate feature that the intensity depends on $|F(hkl)|^2$ and so an accuracy of 4% in intensity corresponds to one of 2% in F values.

The Laue photograph and the early measurements with the spectrometer have been described in former chapters. The story may be taken up at the point where X-ray analysis began to require a large range of *hkl* indices, rather than the accurate measurement of a few reflections.

2. The Rotation Photograph

This classical method was developed by Schiebold and Polányi, and was very widely used in its time (Fig. 1). A crystal is placed at C with one of its principal axes parallel to the vertical arrow in the figure, about which it is rotated. Instead of reflecting X-rays from the face of a large crystal as in the spectrometer, a small single crystal, perhaps of about 0.1 mm³, is used. The crystal is bathed in an incident beam of X-rays, and the cross section of the diffracted beam is determined by the dimensions of the crystal, not by an aperture through which the X-rays pass. The diffracted beams are recorded on a flat plate (*a*) or more conveniently on a cylindrical film (*b*). The resulting spots lie on a series of rows (layer lines). If the axis of rotation coincides with the c axis of the crystal, for instance, there will be a series of layer lines as shown in Fig. 1(*b*). All diffracted beams for which the path difference is l wavelengths will make the same angle with the c axis and so appear on the l layer line.

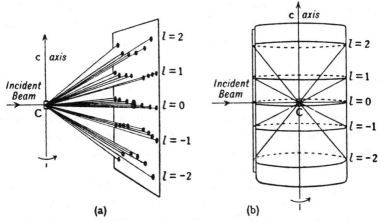

FIG. 1. Layer lines of a rotation photograph (*a*) on a plate, (*b*) on a cylindrical film.

The length of the c axis and the l value for any spot can therefore be deduced at once from the layer lines, though the assignment of h and k values to each spot is less direct. The length of the other axes can be found by placing each in turn parallel to the axis of rotation, and a knowledge of these helps in identification. If there is much overlapping, the rotation can be confined to a restricted arc. A typical rotation photograph is shown in Fig. 2.

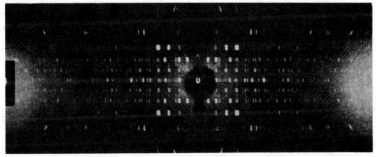

FIG. 2. Rotation photograph of Ettringite (Bannister).

The rotation photograph has come back into use again for an interesting reason. The crystals of macromolecules disintegrate under exposure to X-rays, and it is important to make as many measurements as possible with a crystal while it remains in good condition. The time of exposure is lengthened in the case of photographic methods (see below) which employ screens to select certain reflections in order to facilitate identification. The rotation camera has no such screens, and so the crystal yields the maximum of information before it is spoilt.

3. The Weissenberg Camera

This camera avoids the difficulty of indexing of the rotation photograph by confining the spots to a single zone. Its action can be understood by referring to Fig. 1(*b*). An annular slit on the $l = 0$ level only permits reflections by planes parallel to the axis of rotation to be recorded. While the crystal is rotating, the cylindrical film is translated parallel to its axis, so that the displacement of a spot in the c direction is a measure of the angle at which the crystal was set when the reflection took place, and a knowledge both of the crystal setting and the angle of reflection makes identification certain. Each set of planes in the c zone gives a first order, second order, and so forth, and these orders lie on a slanting straight line, because the angle of diffraction is proportional to the translation of the film. The slanting rows of spots due to sets of planes parallel to c (the 00*l*'s) will be seen in Fig. 3. A Weissenberg exposure records all the spots in a sheet of the reciprocal lattice.

4. The Powder Method

The methods described so far employ a single crystal. The powder method, which was developed independently by Debye and Scherrer in Germany, and by Hull in America, employs a material in which there are many microscopic crystals orientated at random in all directions. This method greatly extended the range of crystalline matter which could be analysed, because there are many substances which are only available in a microcrystalline form. Metals and their alloys are an examples.

The method is illustrated in Fig. 4. A crystalline powder at the centre of the camera P is bathed in the incident monochromatic beam and a cylindrical film around the circumference of the camera records diffracted rays. Amongst the vast number of crystallites some will be so orientated that a given *hkl* reflection can take place and these reflected

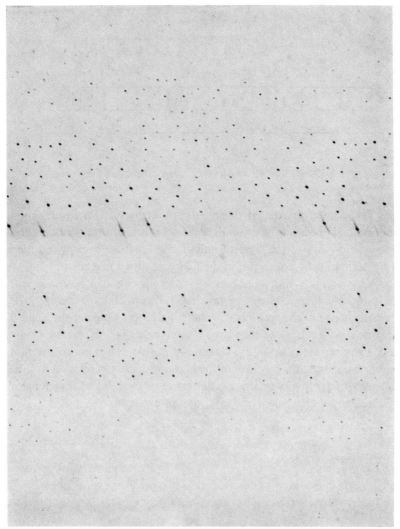

Fig. 3. A Weissenberg photograph.

beams make the same angle with the incident beam, so the reflected rays lie on a cone, of which a small arc is intercepted by the film.

Powder photographs of KCl and NaCl are shown in Fig. 5, with indexed lines. The lines in the NaCl photograph which do not appear in the KCl photograph are the weak reflections with all-odd indices (see page 29).

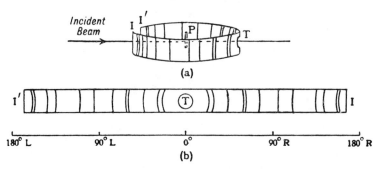

FIG. 4. Powder photograph on a cylindrical film.

The powder is rotated during the photograph. This ensures more uniform lines, because the crystallites pass through a range of orientation. The hole at T allows the incident radiation to enter the camera and there is a system of slits, not shown in the figure, to give a fine beam.

Very accurate measurements of lattice spacing can be made with the powder-camera. When the rays are reflected through nearly 180°, a small change in the spacing 'd' results in a large change of the angle θ, because sin θ changes so slowly as θ approaches 90°. Hence by having at l, l', reference knife-edges, which cast a sharp shadow on the film, and by measuring the position of the high-order lines in relation to these shadows, one gets very accurate estimates of spacing. Jay's measurements of the thermal expansion of quartz are an example.

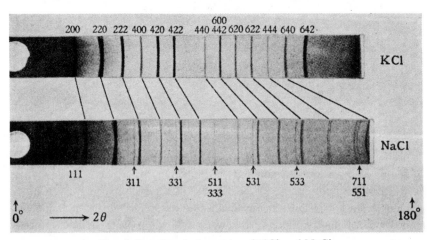

FIG. 5. Powder photographs of KCl and NaCl.

5. The Buerger Camera

This camera is a very elegant device designed by Professor M. J. Buerger for photographing all the diffracted beams corresponding to a plane of the reciprocal lattice. They appear on a network which is an undistorted representation of their positions in reciprocal space, so that indexing is straightforward. The principle of operation is somewhat complex; Fig. 6(a) and (b) may help to explain it.

In Fig. 6(a) a crystal at S is illuminated by the X-ray beam. OP is a central plane of its reciprocal lattice and a sphere is centred at S with diameter $1/\lambda$. As has been shown on page 110, if a point P of the reciprocal. lattice falls on this sphere, there will be a reflection in the direction SP.

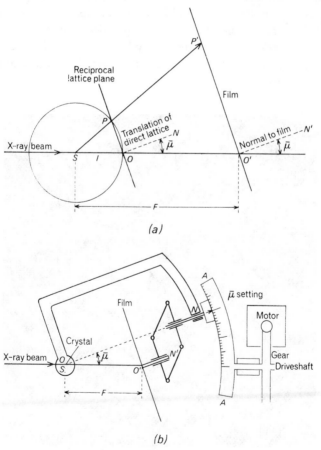

(a)

(b)

FIG. 6. The design of the Buerger precession camera.

The axis in the crystal which corresponds to the reciprocal plane is perpendicular to *OP*. If now the crystal is rocked so that this axis travels round a cone, continuing to make the same angle with *OS*, all the points of the reciprocal lattice within a radius *OP* will in turn fall on the sphere and there will be corresponding reflections. Points on other reciprocal planes will also fall on the sphere, and as the corresponding reflections would cause confusion they are cut off by an annular slit of diameter *OP* (not shown in the figure) which is attached to the crystal holder and only allows rays due to the *OP* reciprocal plane to pass. Next, in order that the representation of the reciprocal net may be undistorted, the photographic film must be kept parallel to *OP*, so that it is perpendicular to the crystal axis. This is achieved by the link mechanism shown in Fig. 6(*b*). The crystal axis is parallel to *ON*, and rocks around its cone as the arm *AA* is rotated by the motor. The link like a parallelogram ensures that the film remains at right angles to the axis. When the camera is in action, the crystal, film, and annular slit perform their gyrations rather like some sinuous eastern dance.

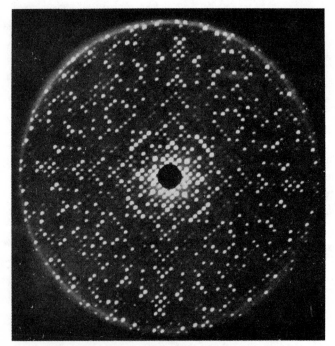

Fig 7. A Buerger precession photograph of the *hko* zone of lysozyme.

A Buerger photograph of lysozyme is shown in Fig. 7: the camera is well suited to recording the diffraction by crystals with large axes, such as this protein crystal, where the diffracted spots are very numerous.

A common device for measuring the intensity of the spots in photographic methods is the multiple pack of films one beneath the other. Each film in the pack diminishes the intensity in a known ratio, for instance by a factor of $2\frac{1}{2}$. A scale of intensity as estimated by eye can therefore be established by comparing the spots on successive films, and it is surprising how accurate such a scale can be if used by a practised observer.

6. The Linear Diffractometer

This instrument which is shown in Fig. 8 was designed by Phillips and Arndt and used for obtaining the numerous measurements needed for determination of the lysozyme structure. In principle it is a mechanical model of the Ewald construction shown in Fig. 3 of Chapter 9. The crystal is set in the right position for a reflection hkl by three screws, one parallel to each reciprocal lattice axis. An ingenious linking mechanism provides that equal increments of turn of a screw move the reflection from one value of h to the next, and the same for k and l. The recording counter is at the same time moved on so as to receive the reflected beams. These movements are controlled electronically by orders given to the machine. It measures the background reflection on one side of a spot, sweeps through the reflecting position and integrates the reflection, measures the background on the other side, subtracts the mean background from the integrated reflection, and records the result on a perforated tape and prints it. The size and complexity of the machine are in impressive contrast to the minute protein crystal, a fraction of a millimeter in dimension, which is the subject of measurement.

The linear diffractometer has the geometrical disadvantage that owing to the method of setting the crystal by the screws, the reflecting planes are not in general parallel to the axis about which the crystal is rotated in getting the integrated reflection. This involves an increased range of rotation and in extreme cases one which is impossibly large, so that such reflections have to be measured with a different setting of the crystal. On the other hand it has the advantage that several reflections on different layer lines can be included in the same sweep. The photograph shows five counters mounted one above the other which are recording five values of $|F(hkl)|$ simultaneously. Such an arrangement not only shortens the time; it also makes it easier to achieve a consistent standard

FIG. 8. The linear diffractometer adapted to measure five reflections quasi-simultaneously.

of measurement, and in the case of protein crystals to get more measurements from one crystal specimen. Since the sensitive protein crystals progressively deteriorate under X-ray bombardment as described above, this is important.

7. The Four-Circle Diffractometer

One of the many instruments of this type is shown in Fig. 9, designed by Arndt. The crystal is orientated by movements around the circles so that the (*hkl*) planes come into the reflecting position and are parallel to the axis of rotation, the ideal position for sweeping through the range of reflection and measuring the integrated intensity. On the other hand the settings of the circles for each *hkl* are much more complex than the straightforward equal increments of the linear diffractometer screws. The angles for each case must be calculated by a computer, and suitable instructions conveyed to the machine.

Fig. 9. The Hilger and Watts four-circle diffractometer.

Machines such as these are becoming so complex, and their design is being changed so rapidly, that no attempt has been made here to describe them in detail. They proceed, like the original spectrometer, by measuring the spectra one by one. As mentioned earlier, it is possible that they may again be replaced in their turn by photographic methods which have come to the fore because densitometry has been so much improved. The densitometry is automated and the results fed into the computer. The electron densities produced by the computer are automatically plotted and contoured. The availability of these automatic methods has made possible an extension of X-ray structure analysis to quite new fields.

CHAPTER 12

INORGANIC COMPOUNDS

1. The Ionic Bond

The first X-ray analyses were of inorganic compounds, and they at once made it necessary to revise the chemical view of the nature of these compounds. The structure of sodium chloride illustrates the new view point.

Till then the Daltonian conception of molecules had been applied to chemical compounds of all types. The equality in the number of atoms of sodium and chlorine when these elements are combined is of course determined by the law of valency. The Daltonian hypothesis supposed that there is a combination of the atoms into 'molecules', each molecule being a pair NaCl. But the structure of NaCl when determined by X-ray analysis showed no evidence of such a pairing. It is a kind of three-dimensional chessboard pattern in which each atom of sodium is surrounded symmetrically by six chlorine atoms and vice versa. I remember well how, at the time I proposed this structure, I was begged by chemical colleagues to find just some slight evidence of a greater interest by a sodium atom in one of its chlorine neighbours than in the five others, in order that the molecular idea could be retained. The idea that typical inorganic bodies consist of oppositely charged ions is now so ingrained in all our thinking that it is difficult to realize how strange it seemed at the time. The following letter, which was written some years later by a famous chemist, may illustrate the doubts felt by those who had always thought in molecular terms.

'Poor Common Salt'

"Some books are lies frae end to end" says Burns. Scientific (save the mark) speculation would seem to be on the way to this state! ... Prof. W. L. Bragg asserts that "In sodium chloride there appear to be no molecules represented by NaCl. The equality in number of sodium

148

and chlorine atoms is arrived at by a chess-board pattern of these atoms; it is a result of geometry and not of a pairing-off of the atoms."

This statement is more than "repugnant to common sense". It is absurd to the n. .th degree, not chemical cricket. Chemistry is neither chess nor geometry, whatever X-ray physics may be. Such unjustified aspersion of the molecular character of our most necessary condiment must not be allowed any longer to pass unchallenged ... It were time that chemists took charge of chemistry once more and protected neophytes against the worship of false gods; at least taught them to ask for something more than chess-board evidence.

Henry E. Armstrong. *Nature* 1927.

A greater understanding of the nature of atomic combination was developing at that time, but was still not widespread. Much earlier in 1904 Abegg had divided chemical compounds into heteropolar and homopolar but it was not until 1916 that Kossel and Lewis explained the nature of these two types of combination. Sodium, for instance, in addition to its two innermost electrons, has eight electrons in a stable outer shell of symmetrical form, and one additional electron, the valency electron, which is only lightly held by the atom and easily detached. Chlorine has seven electrons in its outer shell, one less than the number required for the complete symmetrical shell, and energy is released if an additional electron is absorbed into the shell. When atoms of these elements combine, the valency electron is released by sodium and absorbed into the chlorine structure. This leaves the sodium in the form of a sodium ion, with one positive electronic charge, and chlorine as an ion with one negative charge. The attraction between the oppositely charged ions bind the atoms together in the NaCl crystal. Positive ions are surrounded by negative ions and vice-versa owing to the mutual attractions of the ions. There is no bond between one particular positive and one negative.

Figure 1 shows an interesting early model of the sodium chloride structure, based on Bohr atoms with electrons in orbits. Such atomic models were replaced later by the representation of the electrons as standing waves, but the dimensions of the orbits correspond closely to the distribution of electron density according to the wave model. The larger ions are chlorine, the smaller are sodium, and in each case there are eight electrons symmetrically disposed in the outer shell. It is interesting to note the considerable interspace between the ionic structures.

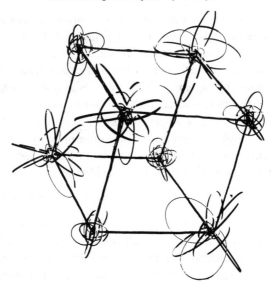

FIG. 1. Model of the sodium chloride structure based on Bohr atoms with electrons in orbits.

The difficulty of accepting this idea, I can remember well at the time, was the conception of positive and negative ions in contact. Why did their charges not neutralize by running from one to the other? It was not fully grasped that electrical charge is always associated with some form of matter, and is not an immaterial 'electrical fluid'. The passage of the electron from sodium to chlorine turns these atoms into charged ions, and so creates electrostatic energy, but this is more than compensated for by the difference between the small amount of energy required to detach the valency electron from sodium and the relatively larger energy released by incorporating it into the outer shell of chlorine.

The idea of the chemical molecule is fundamental in organic chemistry, but its general extension to inorganic compounds in the solid state had in the past been the chief obstacle to an understanding of their true nature. X-ray analysis showed that inorganic compounds are characteristically built of positive and negative ions clustered together. This new conception cast a flood of light on them and removed many misconceptions and difficulties in understanding their constitution.

Homopolar combination, which is the characteristic feature of organic compounds, arises through the fusion of two atomic structures each of which by itself has an incomplete outer atomic shell. This fusion of structure represents the greatest reduction in energy, and so the strongest form of binding, in the combinations of carbon, nitrogen, and oxygen which hence form the basis of organic compounds. Heteropolar combination, the characteristic feature of inorganic compounds, is a combination of stable ions held together by their charges.

2. Ionic Sizes

When ions approach within a certain distance of each other, a force of repulsion sets in which increases very rapidly as the distance diminishes. This force prevents further approach, and makes it possible to assign 'sizes' to the ions.

The author had in 1920 showed that interatomic distances in ionic compounds obeyed an additive law to quite a fair degree of approximation as if ions had characteristic sizes. One could assign radii to them, and the sums of the radii of two ions agreed with the measured distances between their centres to within a few per cent. Unfortunately this first

TABLE 1

2−	1−	0	1	2	3	4
		He	Li 0.78	Be 0.34		
O 1.32	F 1.33	Ne	Na 0.98	Mg 0.78	Al 0.57	Si 0.39
S 1.74	Cl 1.81	A	K 1.33	Ca 1.06	Sc 0.83	Ti 0.64
Se 1.91	Br 1.95	Kr	Rb 1.49	Sr 1.27	Y 1.06	Zr 0.87
Te 2.11	I 2.20	X	Cs 1.65	Ba 1.43	La 1.22	Ce 1.02

Monovalent ions	. NH_4, 1.43	Tl,	1.49	Ag,	1.13		
Divalent ions	. Mn, 0.91	Fe,	0.83	Co,	0.82	Ni,	0.78
	Zn, 0.83	Cd,	1.03	Hg,	1.12	Pb,	1.32
Trivalent ions	. Cr, 0.64	Mn,	0.70	Fe,	0.67		
Quadrivalent ions	. Mo, 0.68	W,	0.68	V,	1.05	Th,	1.10

attempt at establishing sizes was too ambitious. Atoms in homopolar combination as in O_2, N_2, CO fuse their structures together and so the interatomic distance and apparent size is much smaller than that between ions with separate outer shells of electrons. The author tried to make a table for practical purposes which covered both heteropolar (ionic) structures and homopolar structures, and this made all the negative ions too small and the positive ions too large, though the sums of their radii were correct. It was pointed out that the picture of sizes was misleading for this reason and that the positive ions might be much larger, but this defect of physical unreality much diminished the value of the table. Wasastjerna put it right and established the correct datum line between positive and negative ions by his study of refractivities, and ionic sizes were subsequently refined by Goldschmidt in his work on geochemistry.

The above table, from the author's *The Crystalline State* gives the ionic radii of a number of common ions. The dimensions of the ions are shown graphically in Fig. 2, and more complex ions such as CO_3 and SO_4 are included in the figure. In dealing with these latter one must take into account both the close homopolar binding within the ion, and the

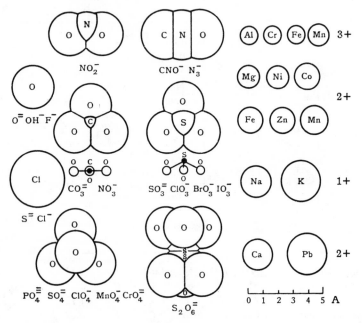

FIG. 2. The structures and dimensions of some acid radicals.

FIG. 3. Crystal models which illustrate the packing together of ions: (*a*) sodium chloride; (*b*) caesium chloride; (*c*) calcite, $CaCO_3$; (*d*) aragonite $CaCO_3$; (*e*) iron pyrites, FeS_2; and (*f*) anhydrite, $CaSO_4$.

heteropolar binding of greater range between the ion and its neighbours. In CO_3 for instance the oxygen atoms are bound very tightly to the carbon. A free oxygen ion has a radius of 1.32 Å, but the binding to carbon makes spheres of this size overlap as seen in the figure.

Figure 3 shows the structure of some simple inorganic compounds, the ions being represented by spheres of appropriate size, and illustrates the way the simple or complex anions are packed together with the cations.

3. Ionic Size as an Aid in Analysis

The concept of ionic size, though approximate, is of great help in analysing inorganic crystals. They must be so packed in the structure that they do not overlap.

Consider first their relationship to the symmetry elements. These elements of planes, axes, and centres of symmetry in a crystal form a framework into which its structure must be fitted. An atom must either lie on a symmetry plane, or at nearest must just touch it, since if intersected by the symmetry plane it would overlap its mirror image which is not permissible. Similarly an atom must either lie on a two-fold rotation axis, or be at least its radius away from the axis, since the two atoms on either side of the axis would otherwise overlap. In the case of threefold, fourfold, or sixfold axes the atoms either lie on the axis or form a ring of three, four or six with the axis through the middle. Similarly an atom must either lie at a symmetry centre or be at a distance from it at least equal to its radius.

A striking case was the analysis of beryl $Be_3Al_2Si_6O_{18}$, in which the solution is immediately apparent because it is the only possible way the ions can be placed in obedience to space group requirements. The structure is hexagonal; Fig. 4(a) shows the scheme of the symmetry elements.

There are sixfold, threefold, and twofold axes perpendicular to the plane of the diagram, as shown in the figure. There is a grid of twofold axes, perpendicular to the c axis and shown as lines in the figure, in planes at heights O, $c/2$, and c. Halfway between these sheets, at heights $c/4$ and $3c/4$, there are reflection planes of symmetry. The figure shows the arrangement of atoms in the upper half unit cell between c and $c/2$. This half cell contains one formula-unit $Be_3Al_2Si_6O_{18}$.

The oxygen atoms are completely pinned down by the symmetry elements. Six of the eighteen (shaded) lie on the symmetry plane at height $c/4$, in a compact ring around the sixfold axis. There is only one other possible place for the remaining twelve. They touch the reflection planes, so that each unshaded circle in the figure represents an atom and its image. Since they must not intersect the two fold axes, they must be jammed in the positions shown between the axes and the reflection plane

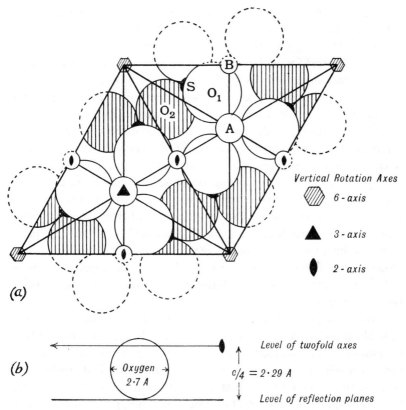

FIG. 4. Deduction of the structure of Beryl, $Be_3Al_2Si_6O_{18}$.

(see Fig. 4(*b*)). The three Be atoms are at the positions marked *B* between four oxygen atoms, the two aluminiums at *A* between six, and the six silicon atoms are on the reflection planes between four oxygen atoms. They are visible as small black segments between shaded and unshaded oxygens.

It is unusual for the symmetry to determine a structure uniquely as in the case of beryl. Symmetry combined with packing is, however, a most useful aid in limiting the possible atomic positions.

4. Coordination

The positive ions in an inorganic compound tend to be surrounded by regular groups of negative ions. The reverse is not in general the case because the negative ions are so much the larger as Fig. 2 shows. Oxygen for example has five times the volume of such ions as magnesium or iron. Typically, the negative ions are packed together in contact and account for the filling of the space, and the positive ions lie in the interstices between them binding the structure together like a cement. This generalization must be qualified in the case of certain large cations such as those of the alkali metals, but it holds for the great majority of salts and minerals.

The most frequent types of coordination are fourfold, where the central atom is inside a tetrahedron, or sixfold, where it is inside an octahedron. Again broadly speaking, the type of coordination depends on the relative size of anion and cation. Four spheres of radius r arranged tetrahedrally can accommodate a sphere of $0.32r$ at the centre, and six arranged octahedrally can accommodate a sphere of $0.41r$. So it is found for instance that manganese, magnesium, iron, cobalt, nickel and chromium generally lie between six oxygen atoms, whereas the small beryllium ion lies between four (see Table 1). Aluminium is a borderline case; it can be between six or four oxygens. Sodium, potassium or calcium require larger interstices, and are found between less regular groups of eight or more atoms. Boron (doubtfully to be regarded as an ion) is found between three oxygens.

The conception of heteropolar and homopolar binding is a useful generalization but must not be pushed too far. In such an ion as CO_3^{2-}, for example, carbon is more naturally regarded as combined in a homopolar way with the three oxygen atoms, than as a minute carbon ion between three oxygen ions. This does not matter as regards structure building, because we only need to consider the whole groups as a complex ion with two negative charges and a size and shape as shown in Fig. 2. Boron is in an intermediate position between carbon, and beryllium, which last is naturally regarded as an ion.

5. Pauling's Rules

These coordinated structures provide a firm datum line for assigning physically justifiable radii to the ions. The measured distances between positive and negative ions are the sums of the radii, so that one could add an arbitrary amount to all the positive radii, subtracting it from the negative radii and still obey the additive law. As has been described above, this led to the author's original misleading table. But there are many cases where the dimensions of the structure are obviously determined by the packing of large negative ions, for instance oxygen, with small metal ions in the interstices, and in such cases the size of the negative ion is fixed unambiguously. Oxygen, for instance, must be assigned a radius of 1.32 Å and once one such datum line is fixed the remainder of the ionic radii follow.

Figure 5 shows four structures in which the oxygen atoms are in close packing with small cations in the interstices. The correspondence in all three dimensions is accounted for by the size of the oxygen ion.

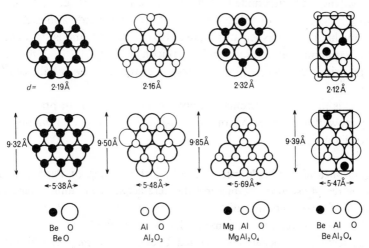

FIG. 5. Successive layers of atoms in the structures of BeO, Al_2O_2 $MgAl_2O_4$. The oxygen atoms are approximately in close packing in each case. The lower layer on the figure is to be superimposed on the upper. The distance between successive sheets is denoted by *d*. The correspondence in dimensions is due to the packing of the oxygen atoms. Note that for Al_2O_2, and $MgAl_2O_4$, additional different layers are necessary to complete the structures.

In 1929 Pauling published a paper 'The Principles Determining the Structure of Complex Ionic Crystals' which was of cardinal importance in establishing the laws governing their structure and stability. The laws of valency demand that there is an overall balance of positive and negative charge in the composition of any inorganic substance. Pauling established a more rigid requirement that these charges balance in detail throughout the structure.

After summarizing the features of ionic size, ionic charge, and co-ordination described above, he showed that the following rule is obeyed exactly or to a close approximation by all stable structures. The positive ion has a cluster of negative ions around it, and one regards its contribution to equalizing the charge on these ions as divided equally between them. The contributions from all the positive ions next to the negative ion are now added, and these are found to be equal or very closely equal to the charge on the negative ion.

The structure of beryl shown in Fig. 4 provides a simple example. Beryllium is divalent, and is surrounded by four oxygen atoms, so its contribution to each is $\frac{1}{2}$ on the scale of the electronic charge. Aluminium is trivalent, and surrounded by six oxygen atoms, so its contribution is also $\frac{1}{2}$. Silicon is quadrivalent and inside four oxygen atoms so each bond has a value 1. The oxygen atoms are of two kinds. The first is surrounded by 1 beryllium, 1 aluminium, and one silicon $(1/2+1/2+1 = 2)$ the other by two silicons $(1+1 = 2)$ so the oxygen charge of $-2e$ is balanced for each.

This at first sight seems a simple requirement, but in practice it is very powerful in weeding out impossible structures, and finding the correct solution.

Significance of Pauling's rule. The physical meaning of Pauling's rule can be readily seen if one pictures the field between the ions in terms of 'lines of force'. The lines of force start from a positively charged body, their number being proportional to the charge in the body, and they end in corresponding negatively charged bodies. They map the electrical field between the bodies. The valency laws ensure that all the lines of force coming from positive ions end on negative ions, because the charges on the ions must balance. Pauling's rule further ensures that the lines of force coming from a positive ion end on nearest neighbour negative ions and vice versa.

The existence of the lines of force in the space between the atoms represents electrostatic energy, and the further the lines have to run in the structure to find opposite charges, the greater will that energy be. Pauling's rule makes the electrostatic energy a minimum because all the lines only have to cross the small gap between neighbouring ions. Structures which obey the rule are stable compared with structures, which are possible by valency rules, but where the atom cannot be so arranged as to satisfy Pauling's rule. It is a basic principle of solid inorganic chemistry.

6. Isomorphous Replacement

One field in which the conception of ionic structures cast a flood of new light was the puzzling question of isomorphous replacement. When the molecular theory of the constitution of inorganic compounds held the field, it was supposed that in mixed crystals there was more than one kind of molecule, and that these molecules were so similar that the one kind could be partly substituted for the other at random without disturbing the structure. This seemed plausible when the substitution was of a simple kind. The alums, for instance, readily form mixed crystals. Their general formula is $R_1^+R_2^{3+}(SO_4)_2 \cdot 12 H_2O$, R_1 being ammonium, potassium, rubidium, caesium, or thallium and R_2 aluminium, chromium, or trivalent iron. One could picture, for instance, ammonium aluminium molecules mixed with potassium aluminium molecules. In more complex cases, however, this would presuppose a very large number of possible molecular types. The general formula of tourmaline, for example, is $X_3Y_{27}B_9Si_{18}H_xO_{93}$. The X position may be occupied by Na_3, Na_2Ca, or $NaCa_2$, with K sometimes partly replacing Na. The Y position is mainly occupied by magnesium, aluminium and lithium, and as regards Mg and Al, the composition varies from $Mg_{11}Al_{16}$ to Mg_2Al_{25}, or if lithium is present there are such compositions as $Li_3Mg_2Al_{22}$, $LiMg_2Al_{24}$, $LiAl_{26}$. Fe^{2+} and Mn may replace Mg, Fe^{3+} or Ti or Cr may replace Al, the total number of ions in the Y position always being 27. $B_9Si_{18}O_{93}$ builds a strong skeleton in the structure in a way to be described below, and there is no variation in this part of the formula. The H ion is unique in that it has no dimensions, being only a proton. It may be incorporated into the O atoms turning O^{2-} into OH^-. F^- can replace OH^-. The number of H atoms in the formula unit may vary between 13 and 5, the number being such as to make the total of positive and negative ions balance in charge. These variations were first studied by Machatschki in 1929 and a list of possible 'molecules' to explain them might well run into thousands.

When one thinks in terms of ionic substitution, however, the variations are readily explained. Ions of the same charge and similar size, such as Mg^{2+} and Fe^{2+}, naturally replace each other readily. When they differ, size is more important than charge, because the ion must fit into a suitable hole in the framework. For instance Na^+ is frequently replaced by Ca^{2+} which is of the same size, and rarely by K^+ which is a considerably larger ion. Li^+ replaces Mg^{2+} in octahedra of oxygen ions. Such replacements must take place in such a way that total ionic charges balance and this may come about through a double substitution of MgSi for AlAl, NaSi for CaAl, LiFe^{3+} for MgMg or NaAl for CaMg. The variety in occupation of the three X positions and the 27 Y position in tourmaline thus receives a simple explanation in terms of ionic replacement.

The difference in nature of inorganic and organic, or heteropolar and homopolar, compounds is again accentuated by isomorphous replacement. The organic molecule is definite. The atoms in it are bound closely and strongly by homopolar bonds, making it an entity, and it is loosely bound to neighbouring molecules; organic crystals are characteristically soft. Isomorphous replacement which so easily takes place in inorganic solids is rare in organic bodies. Precisely similar molecules bind together so much more readily that re-crystallization is a standard method of purification of organic substances.

7. Non-finite Ions

Another conception which originated in the X-ray analysis of crystals has also greatly simplified ideas. It is particularly applicable to silicate structures.

The silicates together with silica compose more than nine-tenths of the earth's crust. In classifying them mineralogists have been mainly guided by their external crystalline form and properties, and not by their chemical composition which often varies very widely. Now that their atomic structure is known, it is clear that the mineralogical basis of classification was the right one. They are divided into certain large families.

The Orthosilicates. A typical member of this family is forsterite, Mg_2SiO_4, generally with some iron replacing the magnesium. Topaz $(AlF)_2SiO_4$ and garnet $Ca_3Al_2(SiO_4)_3$ are other examples. The formula suggests that the anion is $(SiO_4)^{4-}$ like $(SO_4)^{2-}$ in the sulphates.

The Pyroxenes and Amphiboles. These minerals vary widely in composition, but have certain common features in their external properties. Diopside $CaMg(SiO_3)_2$ which has been described earlier, is a typical pyroxene, and another is actinite $NaFe(SiO_3)_2$. The amphibole family has similar physical characteristics. The following general formula, due to Warren who made X-ray analyses of them, indicates the range of variation in their chemical composition.

Amphibole

$$(Ca, Na)_2 \, Na_{0-1}Mg_1(Mg, Al)_4(Al, Si)_2 \, Si_6O_{22}(O, OH, F)_2.$$

An idealized simplification of this formula is

$$Ca_2Mg_5(OH)_2Si_8O_{22}.$$

The general formula is based on the X-ray determination of structure which shows for instance that part of the aluminium is in an octahedral group of oxygens like magnesium, and part in a fourfold group like silicon. They are fibrous in texture, shown in an extreme form by the mineral asbestos.

The micaceous minerals. This is a large family including talc, chlorites, clay minerals and the micas. Simplified formulae are:

Talc	$Mg_3(OH)_2Si_4O_{10}$
Kaolin	$Al_4(OH)Si_4O_{10}$
Muscovite Mica	$KAl_2(OH)_2(Si_3Al)O_{10}$

They are characterized by their platy nature, on a large scale in the micas and a microscopic scale in the clays.

The felspars. The felspars form the bulk of the earth's crust. Typical formulae are

Orthoclase	$KAlSi_3O_8$
Albite	$NaAlSi_3O_8$
Anorthite	$CaAl_2Si_2O_8$

The orthosilicate ion $(SiO_4)^{4-}$ could naturally be supposed to be a separate ion like $(SO_4)^{2-}$ and this was confirmed by X-ray analysis, but what was one to assume to be the negative ions in the other structures? Diopside might be supposed to have an ion $(SiO_3)^{2-}$, but in the amphiboles there is often less silicon than is required by the formula $(Si_8O_{22})^{12-}$. In the felspars there appears to be Si_3O_8 in albite and Si_2O_8 in anorthite yet these are extremes of a range in a series of closely similar crystals.

The solution now seems obvious, but I well remember the great excitement at the time the answer was beginning to be realized, and the doubts with which it was at first received by mineralogists. The structure of diopside provided the first indication. There are no separate $(SiO_3)^{2-}$

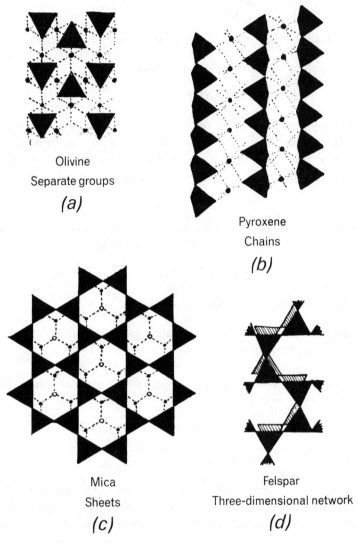

Olivine
Separate groups
(a)

Pyroxene
Chains
(b)

Mica
Sheets
(c)

Felspar
Three-dimensional network
(d)

FIG. 6. Linking of tetrahedra in silicate structures.

ions like $(CO_3)^{2-}$. Instead silicon always lies inside four oxygen atoms at the corners of a tetrahedron, but these tetrahedra are joined by a sharing of oxygen atoms into endless chains which run right across the crystal in the direction of the b axis (see Fig. 6(b)). If we are to retain the conception of ions, these chains must be thought of as parallel linear ions which are bound together laterally by the calcium and magnesium ions. Since two oxygens of each SiO_4 tetrahedra are shared, the ratio of silicon to oxygen is represented by SiO_3. The chain in the amphiboles is like two pyroxene chains joined side by side by a further sharing of the oxygen atoms, reducing the ratio of oxygen to silicon to Si_4O_{11}. Aluminium can proxy for silicon to a certain extent, occupying a similar place inside four oxygen atoms.

The acid radicles in the micas, clays, and similar minerals are infinite sheets, cemented together by cations between them in sandwich fashion.

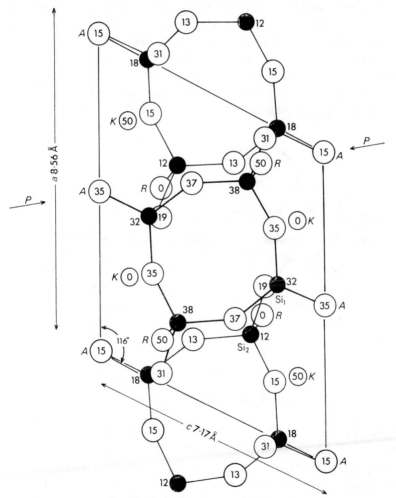

FIG. 7. Typical structure of a felspar.

The tetrahedra share three corners, building up the wirenetting-like structure shown in Fig. 6(c). The lattice of this plane pattern has axes of 5.12Å and 9.0Å and these axes are repeated in all the members of the family though the planes are stacked on each other differently in the various species. The bonds in the sheets are very strong in comparison with those between the sheets, hence the flaky nature of all these minerals.

If all the corners of the tetrahedra are shared (Fig. 6(d)), the ratio is represented by SiO_2. This is the case in the various forms of silica such as quartz. The valencies balance, and therefore there is no place for positive ions in these structures. In the felspars, which are also built of tetrahedra linked by all four corners, some of the silicon is replaced by aluminium. This gives the tetrahedral framework a negative charge, which is balanced by the incorporation of such ions as Na^+, K^+, or Ca^{2+} into the spaces in the network. The ratio is $(Si, Al)O_2$.

In such cases, the negative ion is a three-dimensional framework with cations in its interstices. It is more difficult to picture such frame-

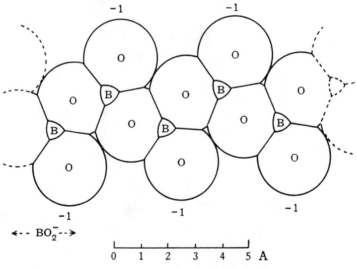

FIG. 8. The negative ion in $CaBa_2O_4$.

works. Figure 7 shows the typical structure of a felspar, first analysed by Taylor. The oxygen atoms at heights 15, 35 in this picture are on rotation axes perpendicular to the diagram and hence form links with the rest of the structure. Similarly the atoms at heights 0, 50 are on reflection planes and form similar links. The tetrahedra are thus linked by all their corners.

The felspars do not contain iron and magnesium, which are such universal constituents of other minerals, and the reason for this is inter- esting. It is geometrically impossible for tetrahedra linked by all their corners to form an octahedral group of six oxygens which Mg^{2-} and Fe^{2-} can occupy, although according to valency considerations their inclusion would be possible. This is an example of the way in which geo- metrical factors govern possible chemical compounds.

Although these non-finite ions are most prominent in the silicates, there are other types. For instance, Fig. 8 shows the linear negative ion the borate CaB_2O_4.

8. The Structure of the Earth's Crust

Although over ninety elements occur in the earth's crust, most of them are comparatively rare, 98% by weight of the crust being composed by the eight most common elements.

Proportion by Weight		Proportion by Volume
Oxygen	46.6	93.7
Silicon	27.7	0.86
Aluminium	8.1	0.47
Iron	5.0	0.43
Calcium	3.6	1.03
Sodium	2.8	1.32
Potassium	2.6	1.83
Magnesium	2.1	0.29

Oxygen is not only by far the most abundant element in the earth's crust (62.5 atomic per cent) but also because of the large size of the oxygen ions compared with those of most of the metals, it occupies 94% of the volume of the crust as shown in the table of volumes. We may consider the crust as a mass of oxygen atoms, held together by a cement of small ions in its interstices.

The bulk of the crust is composed of igneous rocks, the amount of sedimentary rocks being relatively small, and the bulk of the igneous rock is composed of silicates. Felspar forms about 60% by weight of the crust with a density from 2.75 to 2.55, and quartz (2.65), mica (2.86), and the amphiboles and pyroxenes (3.3 to 3.1) account for most of the rest. Olivine has a density of 3.4.

This relative abundance of elements is of course in no way significant of the composition of the earth as a whole. It is held to have an iron-nickel core surrounded by a shell of compounds such as sulphides which are considerably heavier than the silicates. These last, being light and of high melting point, float as a scum on the heavier matter beneath. Amongst the silicates, it is on the whole the lighter which are the more abundant; as would be expected, the 'SiAl' minerals have risen above the heavier 'SiMg' minerals such as olivine. The SiO_4 tetrahedron is the major feature determining this classification. When the mineral contains separate SiO_4 groups, it can be packed much more compactly than when the tetrahedra are joined by corners. The lightest minerals are felspar and quartz where every corner is so joined, and mica (three corners) and the pyroxenes (two corners) lie between the felspars and the heavy olivines. The requirement of sharing corners is more extravagant of space than are independent groups.

The Greeks sought to reduce science to mathematical relations and regular figures. How pleased they would be to note that the fortunate provision of a scum of light matter on which we live owes its origin to the geometrical properties of a tetrahedron.

9. Hardness; Gem-stones

In general, the hardness of an inorganic compound depends upon the size and charge on the ions which form it. The nearer the ions approach and the larger the charges on them, the stronger will be the bonds between them and the harder the structure will be. This assumes that the bonds run in all directions and that the structure is reasonably isotropic. This is far from being the case, for instance, in the micaceous mineral where the bonds are extremely strong in the sheets and very weak between them.

A convenient qualitative measure of hardness is provided by Mohs' scale. It has a standard set of ten minerals chosen such that each can scratch any mineral below it in order, and be scratched by one higher in order, rather like the pecking order in a farm-yard. The minerals are (1) Talc (2) Gypsum (3) Calcite (4) Fluor (5) Apatite (6) Felspar (7) Quartz (8) Topaz (9) Corundum and (10) Diamond. Talc is extremely soft; diamond is the hardest natural substance and is much harder than corundum (ruby, sapphire).

The property of hardness is well illustrated by the gem-stones which are naturally occurring crystals prized for their beauty and precious because of their rarity. There is a bewildering variety of gem-stones with special names, but this is because they are characterized by their colours and these colours are due to various impurities. The number of different crystalline forms is quite small. Apart from diamond, which is a special case, there are only nine crystals which with rare exceptions are used as gems:

Corundum, Al_2O_3
Chrysoberyl, $BeAl_2O_4$
Topaz, $Al_2(F, OH)SiO_4$
Spinel, $MgAl_2O_4$
Beryl, $Be_2Al_2(SiO_3)_6$
Zircon, $ZrSiO_4$
Tourmaline (Na, Ca) (Li, Mg, Fe, Al)$_9$ B_3Si_6 (O, OH)$_{31}$
Quartz, SiO_2
Olivine, Mg_2SiO_4

The colours are in general due to the replacement of Al^{3+} by Cr^{3+} and Fe^{3+}, or Mg^{2+} by Fe^{2+}.

These crystals are all hard:

Corundum 9
Chrysoberyl $8\frac{1}{2}$
Topaz, Spinel 8
Zircon, Beryl $7\frac{1}{2}$
Garnet $7\frac{1}{2}$
Tourmaline, Quartz 7
Olivine, $6\frac{1}{2}$

The compositions explain the hardness, for it will be noted that they are composed of doubly charged oxygen atoms combined with small highly charged cations such as Si^4, B^3, Al^3, Be^2 so that the forces between the close and highly charged ions are exceptionally strong. The hardness of a gem should be greater than 7, for an interesting reason. Dirt contains silica, with hardness seven, and any softer stone would soon have its facets scratched and dulled. Garnet, tourmaline and olivine doubtfully qualify, and for this reason those stones are generally set in brooches or necklaces where they are not so subjected to abrasion as are stones in rings.

To qualify as a gem a mineral must not only be hard, it must be attractive because of its colour or refractive properties. A mineral like phenacite Be_2SiO_4 is hard and it is rare, but it is uncoloured and has a low refractive index, so it is no more attractive than a piece of glass. These requirements explain why so few minerals qualify as gems.

Figure 9 shows refractivity plotted against density and it will be seen that on the whole the refractivity follows the density because the oxygen atoms are responsible for the refractivity and they are more closely crowded in the denser substances. Diamond is quite apart. It

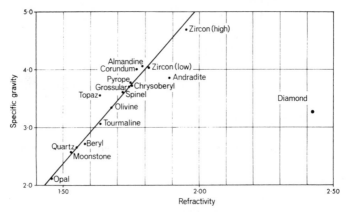

FIG. 9. The relationship between refractivity and specific gravity, in gemstones.

owes its hardness to the strong homopolar bonds between the carbon atoms. It owes its 'fire' to its high dispersion, and a very high refractive index so that all light falling on the face of a brilliant is thrown back by total internal reflection in sparkling colours.

10. Refractive Index

Atomic refractivity. When light waves pass through a transparent body the electric field of the waves polarizes the atoms. The field displaces the positively and negatively charged components of each atom in opposite directions, and so the atom becomes an electric dipole (like a small magnet with north and south poles). In consequence the waves travel more slowly than they do *in vacuo*, because a given electric field produced a greater polarization; it is like an elastic wave passing through a medium in which the elastic response is weaker. The ratio of the velocity of light *in vacuo* to that in the body is the refractive index for light of that particular wave-length.

The contribution of any one kind of atom to the refractive index of a substance can be expressed quantitatively in terms of a constant characteristic of that atom termed its atomic refractivity. The refractive index *in vacuo* is of course 1, and the refractivities of the atoms raise it to a higher value. In calculating how much the atoms become polarized by a field, allowance has to be made for the influence of the polarized atoms on each other. The relationship is given by the classical Lorentz formula:

$$\text{Molecular refractivity} = \frac{M}{\varrho}\frac{n^2-1}{n^2+2} = \text{Sum of atomic refractivities}$$

when n is the refractive index, M is the molecular sum of the atomic weights, and ϱ is the density.

This formula holds good surprisingly well over a wide range of dispersion, for instance the change from liquid or solid to gas. It is convenient to use the molecular refractivity of a body, and not its refractive index, when relating the optical properties of a body to its structure.

As an example of this additive law, the observed molecular refractivities are compared with the sums of the ionic refractivities in Table 2. It will be noted that the refractivities of the cations are in general much smaller than those of the anions, because the electrons are so much more tightly bound in the former.

TABLE 2

	F, 2.20	Cl, 8.45	Br, 11.84	I, 18.47
Li 0.15	2.337	7.587	10.560	15.978
	2.35	*8.60*	*11.99*	*18.62*
Na, 0.74	3.016	8.517	11.560	17.073
	2.94	*9.19*	*12.28*	*19.21*
K, 2.85	5.162	10.846	13.983	19.754
	5.05	*11.30*	*14.69*	*21.33*
Rb, 3.41	6.740	12.549	15.778	21.708
	6.41	*12.68*	*16.25*	*22.88*
Cs, 7.36	9.507	15.572	18.949	25.143
	9.56	*15.81*	*19.20*	*25.95*

Double Refraction. When the light waves pass through a crystal the extent of the polarization for a given field in general depends upon the direction of the field. This is the case because the polarization of each atom depends not only on the electric field of the light wave, but also on the field due to dipole moments of other atoms in its neighbourhood. These atoms are arranged according to the crystalline symmetry, and their effect in one direction may differ from that in another. The polarization thus depends upon the relation of the electric vector to the crystal axes. For any given plane of wave front, there will be a direction of the electric vector for which the polarization is greatest, and a direction at right angles for which it is least. A wave with its field in the first direction travels slower, one with its field in the second direction travels faster, so there will be two refracted beams when light enters the crystal.

This phenomenon of double refraction is displayed by all transparent crystals except those having cubic symmetry, which are 'isotropic' because they have three equal axes at right angles. Now that structures have been analysed by X-rays, it is interesting to trace the connection between atomic arrangement and these optical properties.

The author, in 1924, made a calculation of the refractive indices of calcite and aragonite which explained the double refraction surprisingly well considering the somewhat uncertain physical assumptions on which it was based. The structures, which are shown in Fig. 3(c) and (d), are built on the same plan. There are alternate sheets of calcium atoms and CO_3 groups perpendicular to the trigonal axis in calcite. Aragonite is orthorhombic but pseudohexagonal in symmetry, with alternate sheets of calcium atoms and CO_3 groups perpendicular to the c axis. This similarity in structure is reflected in the refractive indices.

Calcite　　　$\varepsilon = 1.486$ (extraordinary ray with electric vector parallel to trigonal axis)

　　　　　　　$\omega = 1.658$ (ordinary ray with electric vector perpendicular to trigonal axis)

Aragonite　$\alpha = 1.530$ (electric vector parallel to c axis)
　　　　　　$\beta = 1.681$ (electric vector parallel to a axis)
　　　　　　$\gamma = 1.686$ (electric vector parallel to b axis)

The refractive indices of aragonite are greater than those of calcite, but this is accounted for by the greater density of aragonite (2.94) as compared with calcite (2.75). Allowing for this, there is a close correspondence in their molecular refractivities; in the case of ε for calcite and α for aragonite the electric vector is perpendicular to the CO_3 group and in the case of ω for calcite, and the nearly equal β and γ for aragonite, the vector is in the plane of the CO_3 group. This group is clearly being polarized more strongly when the electric field is in its plane than when it is at right angles to the plane.

The values of the ionic refractivities for Ca and O are 1.99 and 3.30. It was assumed that the refractivity of the CO_3 unit was due to three oxygen ions, 2.25 Å apart as determined by X-ray analysis, surrounding a carbon with refractivity zero because it had parted with its outer

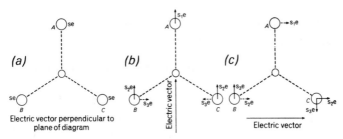

FIG. 10. Polarization of the oxygen atoms in the CO_3 group by an electric field.

electrons to build up the oxygen ions. This is of course a very dubious assumption, but it is partly justified because a similar assumption for many complex ions such as SO_4 accounts for their refractivities.

Figure 10 shows the situation when three oxygens A, B, C are polarized by an electric field. In Fig. 10(a) the field is at right angles to the plane of the group. The lines of force due to the dipole at A curl round and are opposite to the general field at B and C and so they lessen the strength of their dipoles, and similarly B and C lessen the effect on A. Knowing the distance between the atoms one can calculate that the polarization of the three oxygens is only 0.815 times as great as it would be if they were independent.

When the field is in the plane of the group the effect is the opposite (Fig. 10(b) and (c)). In (b) the field of C opposes that at B, but this is more than compensated for by the effect of A. Similarly in (c) the effects of B in increasing C, and of C in increasing B, are dominant. Calculation shows that the net result is a polarization 1.17 times as great as for three separate ions.

This calculation is only a first approximation. The effects of atoms other than those in the same CO_3 group must be taken into account, and to do this rigorously the effects of an infinite series of rows of atoms ought to be summed, a most formidable mathematical task. The author avoided this by calculating with a slide rule the effects of the atoms within ever-increasing spheres around the atom in question, and stopping when the effects of the more distant atoms seemed to be getting so small that they ceased to matter—a classical instance of the physicist's approach rather than the mathematician's!

The net result was to modify the factor 0.815 and 1.17 to 0.87 and 1.12. The refractivities were calculated on this basis for calcite:

Extraordinary ray $R_\varepsilon = 1.99 + 9.90 \cdot 0.874$
Ordinary ray $R_\omega = 1.99 + 9.90 \cdot 1.12$

The calculated and observed refractive indices are compared below.

		Calculated	Observed
Calcite	ε	1.488	1.486
	ω	1.631	1.658
Aragonite	α	1.538	1.530
	β	1.694	1.681
	γ	1.680	1.686

The agreement is probably as good as might be expected from the approximate nature of the physical assumptions which have been made.

Other complex ions. Because of its trigonal symmetry, the polarization of a CO_3 group is the same for any direction of E in its plane. Similarly a group such as SO_4, because of its tetrahedral symmetry, is polarized equally by a field in any direction; it is an isotropic group. In consequence salts with acid RO_4 groups generally have a very weak birefringence. For instance, for $BaSO_4$ the indices are 1.637, 1.638 and 1.649. Incidentally, the refractivity of the SO_4 group in sulphates has an average value of about 13.36, and one quarter of this is 3.34, a value for oxygen closely the same as that assumed for the carbonates.

Optical rotation. Another form of double refraction is shown by bodies which have a threefold, fourfold, or sixfold screw axis of symmetry. Quartz for instance, shown in Fig. 11, has a threefold screw axis. When

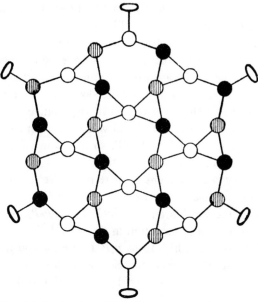

FIG. 11. Projection of the silicon atoms of α quartz.

plane-polarized light travels along the axis in the crystal its plane of polarization is rotated clockwise or anticlockwise depending on whether the symmetry axis is right handed or left handed.

The optical interpretation of the rotation of the plane of polarization is somewhat tricky, but perhaps Figs. 12 and 13 will be of help. In the first place, one can consider a plane-polarized wave as composed of two circularly polarized waves with their electric vectors rotating in opposite

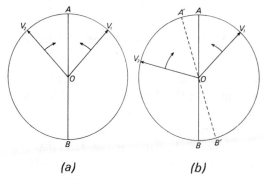

(a)   *(b)*

FIG. 12. Interaction between circularly polarized light waves and an optically active crystal structure. For explanation see text.

directions like the vectors V_1 and V_2 in Fig. 12(*a*). At one moment they coincide along *OA*, and half-a period later along *OB*; the resultant is a plane-polarized wave with electric vector along *AB*.

If these two circularly polarized waves travelled through the crystal at the same rate, their resultant would continue to be along *AB*. If, however, the clockwise wave V_2 is travelling slower than the anticlockwise wave V_1 and so has a shorter wavelength, the relative positions of the vectors at a deeper point in the crystal would be as in Fig. 12(*b*). They will now coincide along *OA'* and *OB'*, so the plane of polarization is being rotated in an anticlockwise direction.

Consider now what happens as these two waves are passing downwards along the trigonal screw axis in a crystal like quartz (Fig. 13). Suppose that at the heights *O*, $c/3$, $2c/3$, P_1P_1, P_2P_2, P_3P_3 represent the directions of easiest polarization in the crystal. They are related by the indicated screw axis, which turns P_1P_1 into P_2P_2, and then into P_3P_3. Suppose that at some moment the electric vector represented by the dotted arrow (2) is at level $c/3$ coincides in direction with P_2P_2. At that

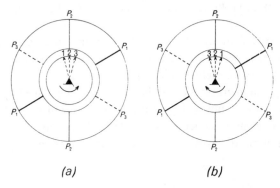

(a)   (b)

FIG. 13. Rotation of the plane of polarization.

moment the vector of the anticlockwise wave at heights P_1P_1 and P_3P_3 will be shown in the figure. For the clockwise rotation the order of the vectors will be reversed as shown in Fig. 13(*b*), being 321 instead of 123. It will be seen that at the level of P_1P_1 the direction of the vector (3) is nearer to the direction of easiest polarization in Fig. 13(*b*) than it is in Fig. 13(*a*) and hence polarizes the crystal more. The same holds for the level of P_3P_3. In their turn these greater or less polarizations affect the polarization at the level of P_2P_2. The net result is that one circular wave polarizes the crystal more than the other rotating in the opposite way, and so these circular waves travel with different velocities. This difference, as has been shown, is equivalent to a rotation of the plane of polarization. It is unfortunate that the same word 'polarization' has by long custom been used to describe the creation of atomic dipoles, and for describing the direction of the electric vector, but it is hoped that the context will make its application clear in each case.

CHAPTER 13

ORGANIC COMPOUNDS

1. The Organic Molecule

The strong homopolar bonds between the atoms make the organic molecule a definite entity, which typically retains its individuality when the solid is melted or dissolved or even vaporized. In contrast, the forms of most inorganic structures only exist in the solid state. The bonds between one organic molecule and another are relatively feeble, hence their crystals are soft, though they have a certain rigidity in such bodies as the sugars with their numerous hydroxyl groups which form polar bonds between molecules. The elements which form the strongest homopolar bonds are carbon, nitrogen, and oxygen in the second row of the periodic table, and they are the main constituents of organic crystals. In order to form part of a continuous structure an atom must be able to form homopolar bonds to at least two neighbours, like oxygen, and to build a three-dimensional network the possible three bonds of nitrogen and four of carbon are necessary. Hydrogen forms only one bond, hence it is a terminating atom which stops further bond formation, like a full stop at the end of a sentence. Because of this function it is, with carbon, nitrogen and oxygen, a main constituent of all organic compounds.

Molecules of every degree of complexity can be formed by these homopolar bonds, because new parts can be added to the structure without breaking existing bonds. These complex structures can have a high energy content, that is to say they may contain much more energy than simpler molecules built of the same atoms. This is in marked contrast to the inorganic compounds, where there are no specific bonds between atoms so that when crystallizing the atoms settle down into a form which represents the lowest energy possible for that particular composition. Dynamite can explode, a mineral cannot do so. Again, because such complex compounds can be formed, life has seized on them for the highly complex molecules needed to perform the many specific tasks in living matter, a feature which gave rise to the title of 'Organic'. The energy of the organic molecule can provide the driving energy for living matter; one can eat bread but not a stone, in spite of the science fiction stories of monsters which crunch up rocks.

2. The Analysis of Organic Molecules

The first X-ray analyses were all made with inorganic structures. Their high symmetry, the known ionic sizes, and the Pauling rules made it possible to investigate structures of quite high complexity. The structure is incorporated in a network of axes, planes and centres of symmetry to which it must conform and this is of great help in analysis.

The organic molecule, on the other hand, is an entity which typically has an irregular shape and no symmetry. Hence most organic crystals belong to space groups of low symmetry, and such elements of symmetry as they do possess are excluded from the interior of the molecule, and only regulate the way the molecules are packed together. In all but the simplest compounds there are a large number of atoms in general positions, so a correspondingly large number of parameters must be determined to define the structure. It is not surprising that their analysis was for long regarded as an almost impossible task.

They have, however, a compensating feature which helps analysis. The atoms are linked by homopolar bonds, and the lengths of these bonds and the angles between them can be established to a high degree of accuracy by the analysis of the simpler structures. If the stereochemical structure is known, that is to say, if it is known which atom is joined to which, the three-dimensional shape of the molecule can often be deduced by using known bond lengths and bond angles. The first X-ray analyses were confined to molecules of known stereochemical structure. All that the analysis contributed was the confirmation of this structure, and a more precise knowledge of bond angles and lengths. It was a long time before X-ray analysis could do more than confirm, since stereochemistry had achieved so much.

A point came, however, when X-ray analysis began to resolve structures where standard chemical methods had failed. Now it is in general justifiable to say that X-ray analysis has taken first place as the most effective and rapid way of solving the structure of a complex organic molecule. Whereas in early days most papers in the scientific literature concerned inorganic structures, they now for the most part are about the structures of organic molecules and macromolecules.

The position forty years ago is illustrated by a paragraph from Vol. 1 of *The Crystalline State* about the analysis of organic compounds, then in a very early stage.

'The main point to be stressed is that complexity of the molecule is no insuperable obstacle to successful analysis. While it would be desperately difficult to find all the positions by X-ray methods alone, these methods may supply just the information which is required to effect a solution when combined with other data. In fact, if X-ray methods are to be of real assistance in organic chemistry, they must be applied to the highly complex substances where purely chemical methods give uncertain results, for the structures of simpler substances are already known. There can be no doubt that an enormous field for investigation exists, and that results of the highest importance are to be expected.'

The finding of atomic positions by X-ray methods alone, described as 'desperately difficult' in this quotation, is now a matter of standard routine owing to the immense advances in the techniques of analysis.

3. The First Analysis

The first attempt to learn something about the structure of an organic molecule illustrates the different approach when compared with inorganic

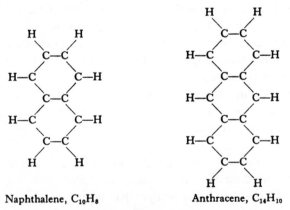

Naphthalene, $C_{10}H_8$ Anthracene, $C_{14}H_{10}$

FIG. 1. Structural formulae of naphthalene and anthracene.
(In this early diagram no allowance is made for double bands.)

analyses. My father in 1921 measured the unit cells of naphthalene and anthracene. These molecules are formed of benzene rings joined as in Fig. 1.

The crystals are monoclinic and the unit cells are closely related in their dimensions, as Fig. 2 shows. The *a* and *b* axes, and the angles β between *a* and *c* are almost identical. The *c* axes are different, being 2.49 Å longer in anthracene than in naphthalene.

He explained these relationships by referring to dimensions in graphite. The structures diamond and graphite are shown in Fig. 3.

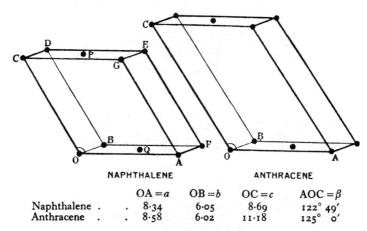

		OA = a	OB = b	OC = c	AOC = β
Naphthalene .	.	8·34	6·05	8·69	122° 49′
Anthracene .	.	8·58	6·02	11·18	125° 0′

FIG. 2. Unit cell dimensions of naphthalene and anthracene crystals.

In diamond the carbon atoms are linked by tetrahedral bonds in all directions, and the structure is extremely hard. Graphite on the other hand is soft and flaky, because the carbon to carbon bonds all lie in the sheets, and not between them.

My father pointed out that the width of the hexagon in the graphite sheet is 2.46 Å, very closely equal to the difference of 2.49 Å for *c* in anthracene and naphthalene, and concluded that the molecules in both crystals are arranged with their long axes in the *c* direction. They pack together side to side in the same way, which accounts for the similarity of *a*, *b*, and β, but the longer anthracene molecule requires a correspondingly longer unit cell in the *c* direction. This conclusion was confirmed when a full analysis of the crystals was subsequently made.

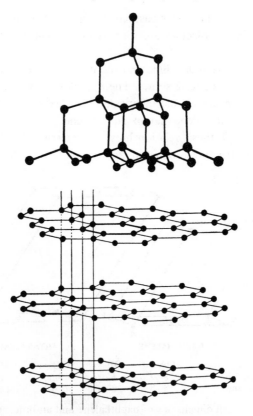

FIG. 3. The structures of diamond and graphite.

4. The Progress of Analysis

Such a vast number of organic structures have been and are being analysed that it is only possible to select examples which indicate the lines along which development has taken place.

The solution of the phthalocyanines by J. M. Robertson and his colleagues in 1935 and succeeding years has already been described in some detail in Chapter 10. It was a very special case in which conditions were ideal for determining the phases (signs in this case) of the F values. The nickel atom which could be added was at a centre of symmetry both of the molecule and of the structure, so that it exerted its full influence in changing all the F values. In general this is not the case for a heavy-atom additive. If the heavy atom is in two or more places in the unit cell owing to the symmetry there will be many cases where its resultant effect will be so small that it is of no help in fixing phase. Phthalocyanine is cited here because it was a first case of a quite complex molecule solved independently by X-ray methods. Robertson and his pupils followed up this success with the solution of a number of other organic molecules of moderate complexity, all of which were in agreement with the constitution which had been assigned to them by the organic chemist, though the analysis gave definition to this form.

As X-ray analysis progressed, however, it approached a point where it could solve problems which had proved intractable by the standard

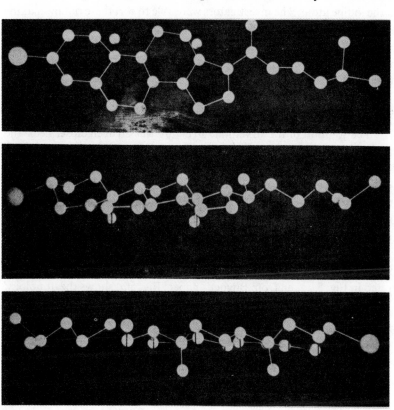

FIG. 4. Photographs of a model of cholesterol iodide.

methods of organic chemistry. This point was nearly reached with the sterols, a series of structures which are important in life-processes. Bernal in 1932 had obtained some indications of their structure, which was till then unknown. A sterol structure was completely analysed by Carlisle and Crowfoot in 1945, but in the meantime it had also been largely established by chemical methods.

The sterol studied was cholesteryl iodide, shown in Fig. 4. It is a strangely shaped long molecule with no centre of symmetry so that the F values can have any phase. The solution was an early example of the use of a heavy atom in a way which has become a standard procedure (see next section). The heavy iodine atom dominates in fixing the phase, and if one assumes the phase to be that due to the iodine alone one gets two superimposed pictures of the molecule, related by a centre of symmetry at the iodine atom. The investigators were able to sort these out by making them conform to known bond lengths and angles, and using such knowledge of stereochemical structure as was available. This was the first of a number of occasions in which Dorothy Crowfoot (later Hodgkin) has advanced X-ray analysis to a next stage of complexity.

5. Strychnine

The solution of the strychnine structure was an even closer neck and neck race. It had been the subject of intense research, particularly by Robert Robinson's school in Oxford, and a number of alternative possibilities had been proposed. Bijvoet and his colleagues in Holland started its analysis in 1947. They succeeded next year in producing a projection of the monoclinic crystal on the b face, and this projection was sufficient to decide which of the alternatives put forward by the chemists was correct. Unknown to them, Robinson had decided definitely on the same model only a few months previously. The form of the structure is illustrated in Fig. 5, taken from Bijvoet's paper; Fig. 5(*a*) shows the 'topology'

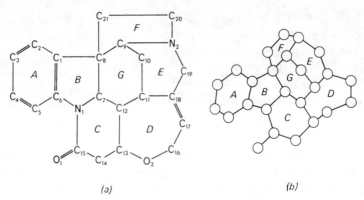

(a)　　　　　　　　　　　　　　(b)

Fig. 5. The structure of strychnine.

of the molecule drawn in the conventional chemical way, and Fig. 5(*b*) shows the structure determined by X-rays. It is a complex cluster of rings tilted with respect to each other, the formula of the unit being $C_{21}H_{22}N_2O_2$.

The strategy of the analysis may be briefly outlined because it is a good example of the method by which such structures can be determined. Bijvoet used strychnine sulphate $(C_{21}H_{22}N_2O_2)_2$ H_2SO_4 $5 H_2O$ and strychnine selenate in which the SO_4 group is replaced by SeO_4.

These crystals are closely isomorphous:

	a	b	c	β
Sulphate	25.7	7.53	7.84	107°20′
Selenate	25.9	7.58	7.90	107°40′

The space group is C2, with a monoclinic unit cell which is centred on the *C* face, and rotation axes parallel to *b*. Looking down the *b* axes at the projection on (010), the S or Se atoms are on the rotation axes and so at centres of symmetry of the structure, with a strychnine group $C_{21}H_{22}N_2O_2$ on either side of the axis, and conditions are very similar to those in phthalocyanine. The signs of the $F(hkl)$ values can be determined directly by noting whether they are increased $(+)$ or diminished $(-)$ when selenium is substituted for sulphur. In this way Bijvoet obtained the (010) projection which, although only a partial solution of the structure, sufficed to decide the correct model.

He then next checked the structure by forming a projection on (001) (a projection along the long *a* axis would be very confused because of overlap of atoms), and the method of obtaining this projection is interesting because it was later to be so universally used in solving protein structures. The projection has no centre of symmetry, so the phases may have any value. The vector diagram in Fig. 6 shows how Bijvoet proceeded.

The origin is taken to be at the sulphur or selenium atom. The scattering by these atoms therefore has zero phase angle, and the difference between the scattering by selenium and sulphur is the vector ΔF in the diagram parallel to the abscissa. The phases relative to the origin of the scattering by the whole molecule are of course unknown, but their amplitudes can be represented by the circles for F(sulph) and F(sel). F(sulph) and ΔF must combine vectorially to make F(sel). This happens at two places in the diagram, one above and one below the abscissa, either of which could represent the wanted phases. This is of course only another way of drawing the diagram of Fig. 10 of Chapter 9. If the centre of the F(sel) circle is moved ΔF to the left, the circles will intersect at the wanted places.

It is not possible to form a simple Fourier map because of this ambiguity of the phases, each of which might have either of the two values determined by the diagram. A map was formed with *both* sets of phases and it is interesting to see what this means physically. If there were a

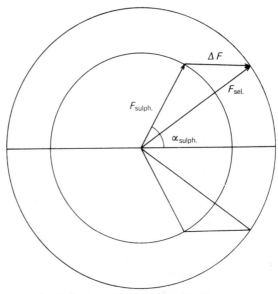

FIG. 6. The single isomorphous replacement method applied to the determination of phases in the study of strychnine.

centre of symmetry at the position of the heavy atom, each strychnine unit would be repeated as an image on the other side of the centre. Therefore if a Fourier synthesis is formed with both sets of phases it will show not only the true unit but its image as well because one of the possible F values in each case comes from one unit and the other F value from its image. This is equivalent to using only the real parts of the vectorial F's in Fig. 6, because the imaginary parts parallel to the ordinate axis above and below cancel out. (Since the heavy atom is now at a centre of symmetry all phases must be plus or minus.) It was found possible to sort out this double image by comparison with the (010) projection, since the x parameters were common to both projections, and so all three coordinates of each atom could be fixed.

Bijvoet remarks 'In order to avoid the double model the replacement model could be extended as follows. Consider three substances, (I)α-chlorine strychnine sulphate (II) α-chlorine strychnine selenate and (III) α-bromine strychnine selenate which are isomorphous. Now comparison between (I) and (II) will give two possibilities for the phase angle of every reflexion of substance (I). Comparison between (I) and (III) will also give two possibilities for the α values of (I). If both ΔF values are different —and mostly they are—the two pairs of α values must have one in common. So for nearly every reflexion the α value can be determined and one model will result.'

This is of course precisely the principle which has been used in determining protein phases by measuring the effect of several different heavy atom additions.

6. Absolute Configuration of Optically Active Molecules

Another landmark in 1950 was also due to Bijvoet, who established the absolute configurations of dextro and laevo compounds. Asymmetrical chemical molecules exist in two forms which are identical in every way except that the one is the mirror-image of the other, like a right hand and a left hand, or a right-handed screw and a left-handed screw. No orientation can make the one superimpose upon the other. Such molecules are optically active; a solution of the one form twists the plane of

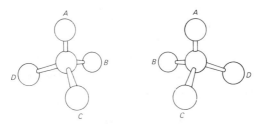

FIG. 7. The arrangement of atoms about an optically active carbon atom: one form is the mirror image of the other.

polarization of light in one direction, and the other form twists it equally in the opposite direction. A simple example is a carbon atom attached to four different units at the corners of a tetrahedron. The two forms shown in Fig. 7 are mirror images of each other; no twisting them about can make them appear the same.

The chemists have adopted a convention for terming one set of configurations 'dextro' and the other 'laevo'. Organic compounds are so inter-related that if a conventional way is chosen for any one of them it will decide the form, dextro or laevo, of all the rest. There was no way of deciding, however, whether the forms assigned to the dextro compounds were the actual forms in Nature, or their mirror images.

A normal X-ray diffraction picture cannot distinguish between a dextro and a laevo crystal. The amplitude of a given reflection hkl depends upon the scattering power of the atoms and the phase differences of the wavelets scattered by them. If now we consider the reflection $\overline{hkl}$ from the other side of the planes, we note that all the phase angles are reversed in sign because a wave path which was longer in the first case becomes shorter in the second, but their magnitudes remain the same and the *amplitude* of the resultant is not altered; the reflections hkl and $\overline{hkl}$ are equal in intensity. The X-ray measurements add, as it were, a centre of symmetry to the crystal. Laue remarked in his original paper that in the first pictures of zincblende the crystal seemed to have complete cubic symmetry although its actual symmetry is tetrahedral, with no centres, and the reason for this was pointed out by Friedel.

This equality of the reflections hkl and $\overline{hkl}$ holds as long as phases are those to be expected for waves scattered at the atomic centres. This is in general very nearly true, but there is a marked departure when the wave length of the radiation is slightly less than the absorption edge (Chapter 3) of an atom. The scattered radiation then differs in phase from what would be expected for radiation from the atomic centre, as if the path difference were less, or the atom displaced towards the side on which reflection is taking place. The values of $F(hkl)$ and $F(\overline{hkl})$ then differ to a degree which can be measured. In Fig. 8 an atom which scatters anomalously is at B and the reflection from all the rest of the structure is supposed to come from the reference plane. For the hkl reflection, B will scatter a wave as if it were centred at B', further from the planes, whereas for the $\overline{hkl}$ reflection it will appear to be at B'' nearer to the plane. The resultant amplitude got by combining the effects of A, B and C will clearly be different.

Fig. 8(d) shows Bijvoet's vector picture of the same effect. An alteration of phase in the scattering of an atom is equivalent to combining the normal f of an atom with a vector Δf at right angles to it, which swings round the vector through a small phase angle. The diagram illustrates how the difference between $F(hkl)$ and $F(\overline{hkl})$ arises.

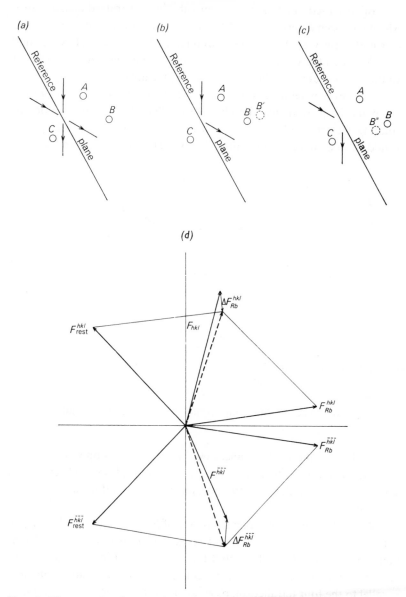

FIG. 8. The genesis of anomalous scattering differences between $F(hkl)$ and $F(\bar{k}\,\bar{h}\,\bar{l})$.

Bijvoet used crystals of sodium rubidium tartrate the structure of which had been determined by Beevers and Hughes. The absorption edge of rubidium is 0.81 Å and when zirconium Kα radiation of wavelength 0.78 Å is used the value of ΔF in Fig. 8(d) is equivalent to 3.2 electrons so the differences in F values were quite appreciable.

By noting whether F was weaker or stronger for a number of hkl, $\overline{hkl}$ pairs, he proved that the absolute configuration of normal dextro-rotating tartaric acid is that shown in Fig. 9. The OH and H groups would be interchanged in its mirror image. This decision agreed with the

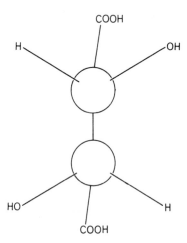

Fig. 9. The absolute configuration of the tartaric molecule.

chemical convention. The chances were even that the opposite would be the case and it is most fortunate that the right convention had been chosen since otherwise the dextro-laevo assignments would all have to be inter-changed.

A simple way of regarding the power of X-ray analysis to distinguish between dextro and laevo forms is to consider the group of four different units arranged tetrahedrally around a carbon atom in Fig. 7. If one of them scatters anomalously, and the reflection from planes approximately parallel to the four tetrahedron bases are measured, one can determine in each case whether the anomalous unit is, so to speak, at the front or the back and so place the units correctly at the four corners.

7. Penicillin and Vitamin B₁₂

These two famous X-ray analyses were outstanding at the time they were made. The solution of penicillin by Hodgkin and Bunn was the result of four years' close collaboration between chemists and crystallographers. The compound was of great interest because its use in medicine was so novel and important. To quote from the original paper 'Throughout the whole of the X-ray investigation of penicillin we have been working in a state of much greater ignorance of the chemical nature of the compounds we have had to study than is usual in X-ray analysis.' It is interesting to note that, amongst the X-ray techniques which were employed, the 'fly's eye' described in an earlier chapter played quite an important part. The structure is shown in Fig. 10.

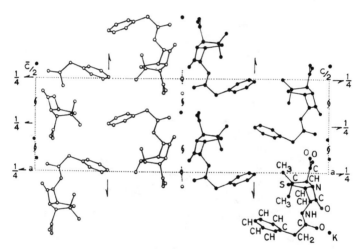

FIG. 10. The structure of potassium benzyl penicillin.

The structure of Vitamin B₁₂, $C_{63}H_{84}N_{14}O_{14}PCo$, was solved in 1957 after eight years study by Mrs Hodgkin and her colleagues. It was recognized as far in advance of anything that had so far been made, and helped to earn the award of the Nobel Prize. This was a case when the establishment of the structure was mainly due to X-ray analysis. There is a cobalt atom at the centre of the molecule which is surrounded by four rings, three of them sixfold and one fivefold is shown in Fig. 11(*a*), an asymmetry which was not expected chemically. The analysis was based on the heavy cobalt atom. Fig. 11(*b*) shows a complete molecule.

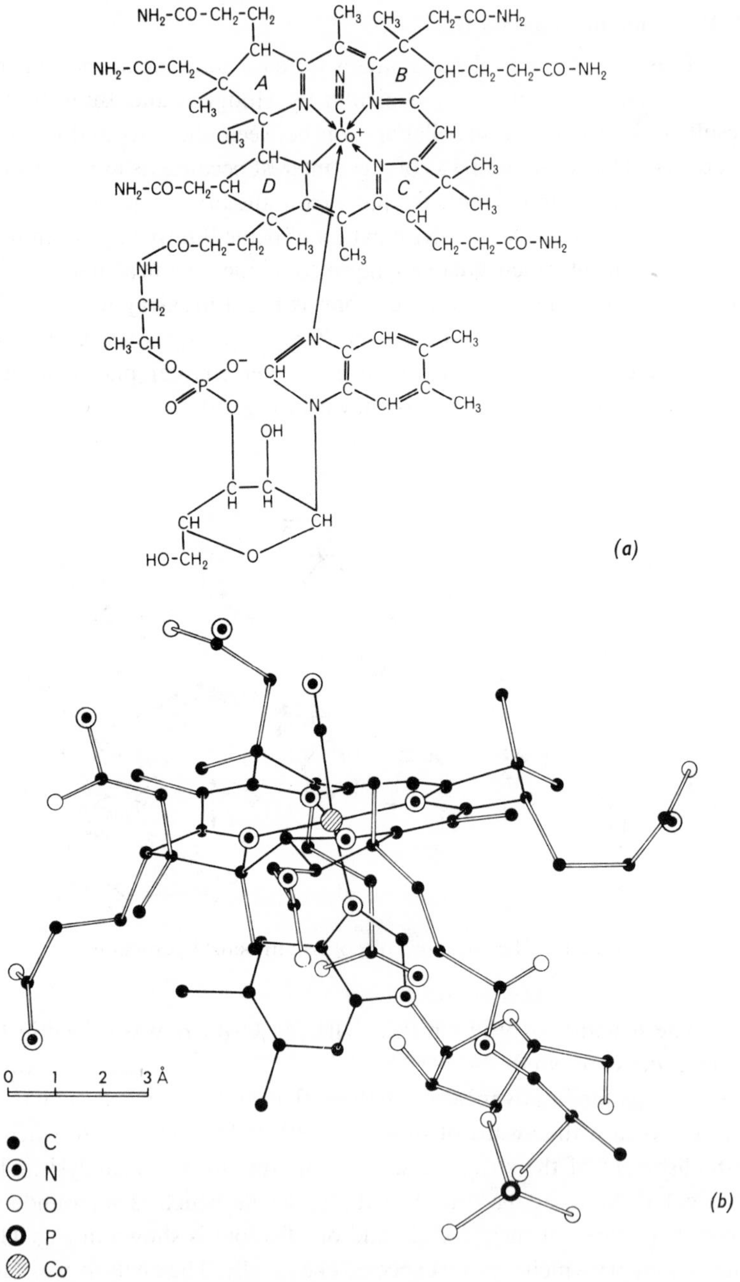

(a)

(b)

- ● C
- ◉ N
- ○ O
- **O** P
- ◍ Co

0 1 2 3 Å

FIG. 11. The structure of vitamin B_{12}.

8. X-ray Analysis as a Standard Method

X-ray analysis has become a standard method of solving the structures of organic compounds of unknown chemical constitution. The most commonly employed line of attack is by the heavy-atom method described in Chapter 9. It is nearly always possible to attach a heavy atom in some way, such as bromine or iodine in ionic form or incorporated in a complex such as the iodoacetate. The position or positions of the heavy atom in the unit cell are readily found, for instance by Patterson synthesis where their vectors stand out from the rest. The phases are first taken to be those due to the heavy atoms alone and a Fourier synthesis is formed. Although it is a poor approximation, it reveals the positions of some of the lighter atoms particularly those in the neighbourhood of the heavy atoms. These are included in the next synthesis, and so by a process of refinement the whole structure is revealed.

A vast number of complex organic molecules, of previously unknown chemical constitution, are now being analysed. As an example, the work of J. M. Robertson's school at Glasgow may be cited. The molecules examined, many of them natural products, contain some thirty or forty atoms apart from hydrogen, and in nearly every case the heavy-atom method was used.

Figure 12 shows the structure of clerodin, analysed in the form of clerodin bromo-lactone. The constitution and stereochemistry of this compound are shown in Fig. 12(*a*), that of clerodin itself in Fig. 12(*b*), and the X-ray Fourier synthesis on which this structure is based is shown in Fig. 12(*c*). The Fourier synthesis is three dimensional, and in Fig. 12(*c*) superimposed sections are shown at convenient heights to reveal the position of the atoms. The very heavy atom at the upper left is the bromine atom.

Figure 13 shows a similar analysis of the stereochemistry and electron density in the alkaloid caracurine, in this case in the form of the dimethiodide; the two heavy iodine atoms can be seen.

The process of analysis would be impossibly laborious were it not for the availability of the electronic computer. Trial Fourier series can be summed and plotted, and the *F*'s for a trial structure can be calculated, so quickly that the process of refinement is rapid. Many of these structures have been the subject of long and laborious chemical examination which has only yielded uncertain results; the examination of the substances in crystalline form by routine X-ray methods is becoming much more

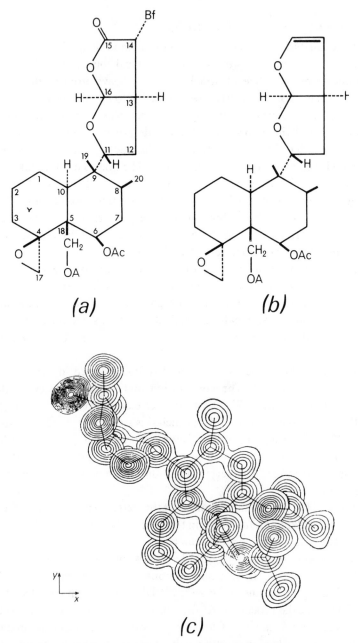

FIG. 12. The structure analysis of clerodin.

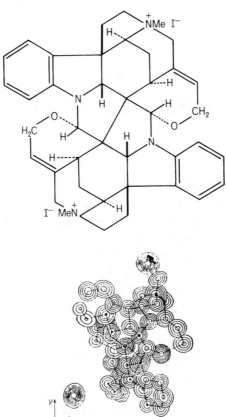

FIG. 13. The structure analysis of caracurine.

direct and precise. Indeed, the process of solving structures of molecules containing fifty to sixty atoms by the heavy atom method has become so standardized that it has been found possible to frame programmes so that the whole process is done by computer. The X-ray measurements are fed into the machine, and it carries out the routine of first approximate structure and successive refinement. If this becomes the standard practice, one cannot but have some regrets that such a fruitful source of subjects for Ph.D. theses, the analysis of an organic molecule, must now be abandoned.

CHAPTER 14

METALS AND ALLOYS

1. Characteristic Metallic Properties

There are certain typical properties of metals and alloys which distinguish them from other forms of matter, and which are recognized as coming under the general heading of 'metallic'.

One set of these properties is based on the atomic constitution of the metal. Metals are good conductors of electricity, and have a high reflecting power for light which gives them their characteristic metallic lustre. They are also very opaque to light. They mix readily to form alloys, and the laws which govern the way they combine are very different indeed from those governing organic or inorganic compounds. The composition of an alloy phase is often variable over quite a wide range and they are non-Daltonian in that the proportions are often not expressible in simple numbers. They are always crystalline. This is not often obvious from the outer form, but it is apparent if they are etched or analysed by X-rays.

Another group of characteristic metallic properties is exhibited by their large-scale mechanical behaviour. Metals can be ductile. If stressed beyond their yield point they deform and deformation does not cause rupture. The metal is as strong afterwards as it was before, and in fact in many cases the metal is toughened by what is termed 'cold work'. A pure metal, which has been coaxed into a regular crystalline pattern by heating and slowly cooling, or annealing, can be very weak indeed and will yield to very small shearing stresses. If deformed, however, it becomes strong. Small amounts of impurity make a very great difference to a metal, sometimes converting the soft pure metal into an elastic or a brittle state. Such properties depend on the previous history of the metal. For instance a piece of steel can be made elastic by heating and then cooling at a suitable moderate rate and if deformed it springs back to its original shape. The same piece if cooled very slowly becomes soft and can be permanently bent. If cooled very fast, as by plunging it into water, it becomes brittle and snaps if an attempt to bend it is made. A file if slowly annealed becomes soft and the grooves can be imprinted on it in a press. When heated and rapidly quenched it becomes glass-hard and is able to cut other metals.

These two groups of properties are often labelled as 'structure independent' and 'structure dependent'. Structure in this sense does not mean atomic arrangement, but what might be called the 'geography' of the metal such as the arrangement and size of its crystallites, and the dislocations and faults in the crystallites due to strains and distortions.

The unique toughness and dependability of a metal, and the way in which its properties can be 'tailored' to meet requirements, have made it the basis of technological advance. Before metals were available man had to rely on natural products such as stone, wood, hide, hair, bone and sinew to make his weapons and appliances. Metals are not natural products, and the discovery of how to produce them artificially made such a difference that we talk of 'The Bronze Age' and 'The Iron Age' as stages in social development.

2. The Physical Nature of a Metal

A metal is essentially composed of electropositive atoms. The isolated neutral atom has one or more loosely held electrons, called valency electrons, which are easily detachable and give it its electropositive character. When such atoms are brought together, the valency electrons are, as it were, thrown into a common stock, and the result is a complex of positive ions held together by the continuous sea of electrons between them. It is this nature, so very different from that of inorganic and organic compounds, which gives the metal its unique properties. There are no bonds between atoms; on the contrary, the ions repel each other. The metal is a compound between the positive ions of all kinds on the one hand, and the electrons on the other. Hence the laws of combination are governed by entirely different factors. Since there are no bonds, the atoms readily assume a crystalline pattern. For the same reason, the metal structure reforms after distortion and, as it were, heals its wounds becoming continuous again; so the metal is ductile.

The X-ray analysis of the atomic arrangement in metals and alloys has done much to explain the 'structure independent' properties of metals. In particular, it has made it possible for the theoretical physicists to analyse the laws of metallic combination in alloys and so has for the first time provided a rational basis for metal chemistry.

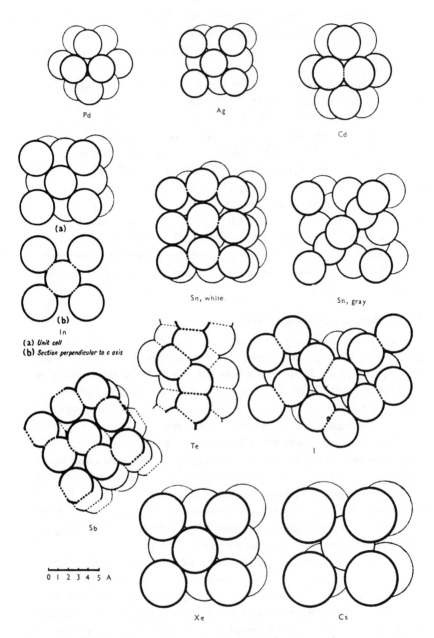

FIG. 1. Structure of elements from palladium to caesium.

On the other hand it has been of little help in explaining the all-important 'structure-dependent' properties of metals and indeed there is no satisfactory quantitative theory of the mechanical properties. Considerable advances have been made in improving them but the progress has been empirical. It has not been possible, for instance, to calculate theoretically how much a given addition of a foreign element will raise the yield-point of steel; it would be of the greatest importance to make this calculation because one could then calculate theoretically what limit of strength one might hope to attain. Much effort and thought has been put into this problem but the results have been disappointing. It still awaits the genius who will show us how to attack it by some hitherto unguessed approach.

3. The Elements

Figure 1 shows as an example the structure to scale of the elements from palladium to caesium. The atoms are drawn as spheres in contact touching where the distance separating nearest neighbours is greatest, and overlapping as shown by the dotted lines for lesser interatomic distances. It is a very instructive series.

The simple construction of a typical metal as an assemblage of positive ions in a general sea of electrons leads to a correspondingly simple crystal structure. Many metals have the cubic or the hexagonal close-packed structure shown diagramatically in Fig. 1 and as models in Fig. 2. These two forms are equally compact. The layers shown in Fig. 2 are close-packed sheets in which each atom is surrounded by six others. If stacked as in Fig. 2(a) the resulting structure has cubic symmetry, if as in Fig. 2(b) it has hexagonal symmetry. Another common form of packing is the body-centred cubic illustrated by caesium. This form is slightly less economical of space than the forms of closest packing.

The transition metal palladium is in hexagonal close-packing. Silver has face-centred cubic close packing. Cadmium approaches closely to a hexagonal close packing, but the layers perpendicular to the hexagonal axes are slightly compressed as shown by the dotted lines. Indium approximates to cubic close packing, but is tetragonal with compression of the layers perpendicular to the c axis.

At this stage in the series a tendency towards homopolar binding as opposed to close-packing begins to be evident. White tin is still metallic in character but gray tin has the diamond structure, every atom being between *four* others. Each antimony atom has *three* nearest neighbours,

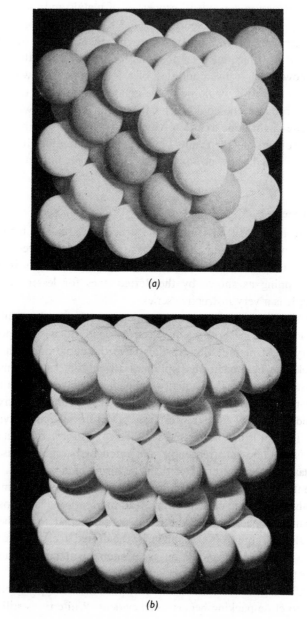

(a)

(b)

FIG. 2. (*a*) cubic (*b*) hexagonal closest packing of equal spheres.

each tellurium atom *two* so that they are in strings, and each iodine atom is bound to *one* other to form I_2 molecules. This 4, 3, 2, 1 rule for neighbouring elements in the periodic table was first pointed out by Bradley.

In xenon the atoms are held together by weak Van der Waals forces in cubic close packing. The alkali metal caesium has body-centred packing. The last illustrates the considerable difference between the size of the transition metals and their neighbours, on one hand, in which the outer electronic shell has 18 electrons or a close approximation to this number, and the alkali metals on the other hand when the outer shell has eight electrons. The latter are much larger.

The structures illustrate a point which must be stressed; the classification of interatomic forces as Van der Waals, ionic, homopolar, and metallic is artificial, though a very convenient approximation. All bodies are a collection of nuclei and electrons, and they are held together because the electrons are in states of lower energy when the atoms are near each other than when they are dispersed. There is no difference in principle between the type of combination. At some point in the series of Fig. 1, the metallic compound shades over into one which is homopolar in character, but this point cannot be defined. The classification is only justified by its convenience.

4. The Structure of Alloys

Westgren in Sweden was a pioneer in analysing alloy structures by X-ray analysis from 1921 onwards. Bradley, who had studied under Westgren, followed up his work and his school in Manchester was responsible for most of the earlier advances on which the study of alloys is based.

The ideal method for studying alloy structures is the powder-photograph technique devised by Debye and Scherrer, and by Hull. It is rarely possible to study a single crystal of a metal or an alloy, as they are nearly always microcrystalline. Filings of the specimen are made into a thin cylinder at the centre of the powder camera, and this is rotated during the exposure so that all planes have a chance to reflect in all possible orientations giving lines that are continuous. When crystals have a low symmetry the *hkl* reflections are very numerous and hard to index, but fortunately most alloy structures have a high symmetry so this usually presents no problem.

Fig. 3 due to Westgren, illustrates an early examination of the silver-cadmium alloys by the powder method. The films were exposed in the

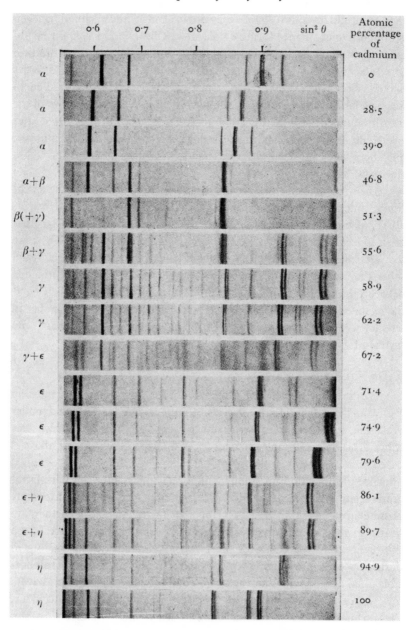

Fig. 3. An X-ray examination by the powder method of the silver cadmium alloys (Westgren). FeK radiation. (From a paper by J. Westgren and G. Phragmén, Metallwirtschaft (1928) VII, 700–703.)

type of circular camera described in Chapter 11, and only the portions at higher angles of reflection are reproduced here. The values of $\sin^2 \theta$ are shown at the head of the diagram; $\sin^2 \theta$ would be unity for a reflection through 180°.

Starting with silver at the top, the structure remains one of cubic close packing (α) until the atomic proportion of cadmium rises to about 40%; the cadmium is said to be in solid solution in the silver. The addition of cadmium merely increases the lattice spacing, as shown by the movement of the lines to lower angles. It will be noticed that as $\sin^2 \theta$ approaches unity the resolution becomes very high as shown by the separation of the lines of the $K\alpha$ doublet, since in this region a small change in spacing or wavelength causes a large change in θ. As the cadmium content is further increased a new phase which is body-centred cubic appears, while the amount of α phase decreases. At about 50% the structure is pure β. Beyond this point a γ phase sets in which is the only phase around 60%. This is followed by hexagonal phases ε and η. There is an alternation of single phases with two-phase regions between them. These intermediate regions represent a mixture of the two phases on either side, in a proportion which varies from all of one kind to all of the other.

Some of the regions of single phase extend over a wide range of composition, like the α phase in this case; others are narrow and correspond to simple atomic proportions like the β phase which is nearly AgCd. It had been usual to term a case like the α phase a 'solid solution' but there is no basis for such a distinction since there are all grades between the two extremes.

These single-phase and two-phase regions were originally identified by a metallurgical examination of polished and etched alloy surfaces. X-ray analysis subsequently showed that each phase is characterized by a definite arrangement of the atoms. The arrangements of α, β, γ, ε, η are shown in Fig. 4. α is face-centred cubic like silver itself, β body-centred cubic, γ a complex cubic structure with 52 atoms in the unit cell, ε is hexagonal close-packed, and η a similar structure elongated along the hexagonal axis like pure cadmium.

Phase regions. We have seen in the previous section that, in a binary alloy system, only one or two phases can coexist at a given temperature. This result can be deduced by considering the variation with composition of a thermodynamic quantity called the free energy, the general rule

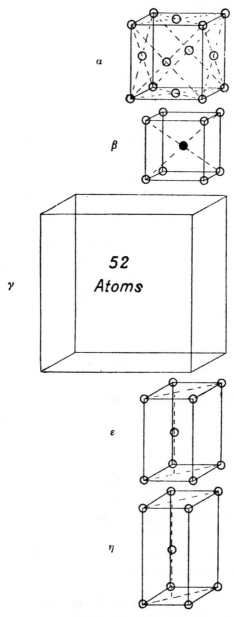

FIG. 4. Structure of the silver cadmium alloy phases (from a paper by Westgren and Phragman, *loc. cit*).

being that the stable form of an alloy is that which makes the free energy a minimum. We do not need to know what the free energy is; we merely need to assume that it has a continuous variation with composition, and that different phases have different free-energy curves.

The principle is illustrated in Fig. 5, which shows three curves, X, Y, Z, representing the variation of free energy per gram-atom for three phases that could be formed from two metals A and B; the first α

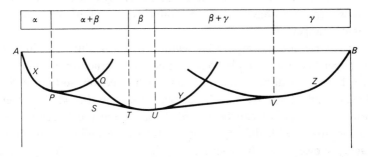

FIG. 5. Variation of free energy per gram-atom for three phases that could be formed from two metals, A and B.

is a solid solution of B in A, the second, β, is an intermetallic compound with a range of solubility, and the third, γ, is a solid solution of A in B. Since the curve for β is below that for α beyond the point of intersection Q, α cannot be the stable form beyond Q. But neither is the phase β itself, for a still lower free energy can be obtained by mixing α and β; the free energy of a mixture is represented by a point such as S lying on a line joining the separate free energies. The lowest such line is PT which is the common tangent to the curves X and Y. Thus up to P alloys will be single-phase (α), from P to T two-phase ($\alpha+\beta$), from T to U single-phase (β), from U to V two-phase ($\beta+\gamma$) and from V to B single-phase (γ).

Any phase will have a free-energy curve, but unless it intersects the curve $APTUVB$ it will not exist as a stable form; it may be metastable. The relative positions and shapes of the curves may change with temperature, so boundaries will change and new phases may appear and disappear; then we have reactions in the solid state, well known to metallurgists.

5. Types of Phase

As more phases were analysed by X-rays the problem presented by their structures became very intriguing. Interest was especially focused on structures like the γ phase in the silver-cadmium series described above. Phases which resembled it closely in physical properties occur in alloys of copper, silver or gold with zinc and cadmium, and with aluminium and tin. They occur in alloys of iron, cobalt, or nickel, or with the palladium or platinum triad of metals with zinc. X-ray analysis showed that all these structures have unit cubes containing 52 atoms with the same atomic arrangement.

The structure has a puzzling feature, which is illustrated in Fig. 6. The upper figure is a simple body-centred cubic structure in which three cubes have been stacked side by side in each direction, so that there are 27 cubes and 54 atomic sites. It has been drawn in this way in order to show that the atoms can be regarded as making the larger unit cell, and the atoms with different symbols then have different separations. Bradley showed that the γ structure (Fig. 6(*b*)) is very closely related. To arrive at it an atom at each corner of the large cube and one at its centre, marked by crosses, are removed and the remainder of the atoms make small movements towards filling up the gaps so created. For instance, the four atoms marked as black circles close in when the central atom is removed. To sum up, the structure is very nearly body-centred cubic, but with one atom in every 27 taken away. What is the particular merit of this strange complex structure which causes it to appear in so many alloy systems?

There are further strange features. Bradley made a close examination of the related structures Cu_5Zn_8, Ag_5Zn_8, Au_5Zn_8, and Cu_5Cd_8 and discovered a surprising fact. Although the sites for atoms are arranged in the same way in these structures, the distribution of the monovalent and divalent atoms between the sites in the zinc alloy is quite different from that in the cadmium alloy. There are four types of site in Fig. 6(*b*), on which the 52 atoms in the unit cell are distributed:

> 8A positions marked as black circles
> 8B positions marked as white circles
> 12C positions marked as white squares
> 24D positions marked as black squares

In the alloys of copper with zinc, the 8A position and 12C position (20 in all) are occupied by the copper and the 8B positions and 24D

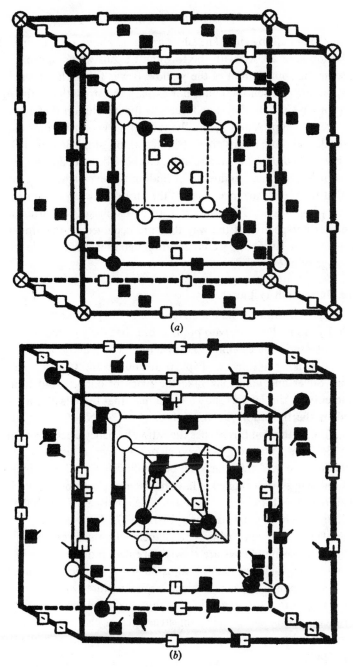

FIG. 6. (a) the derivation of the structure of γ-brass from a simple cube-centred arrangement of atoms. (b) structure of gamma brass (Bradley and Thewlis, Proc. Roy. Soc. *A112*, 678–92, 1926).

positions (32 in all) by zinc. The silver and gold alloys are the same. This distribution is in accord with the formula Ca_5Zn_8 which approximately represents the composition of the γ alloy. It was found, however, that a corresponding distribution could not explain the strengths of the $F(hkl)$ values for Cu_5Cd_8. Bradley was forced to the conclusion that 16 copper atoms are in groups A and B, and the remaining 4 copper atoms together with the 32 cadmium atoms are distributed amongst the 36 C and D sites, probably at random. This investigation has been described in some detail because it had a crucial influence in finding the explanation. It became clear that the precise arrangements of the atoms between the sites was of secondary importance. The primary feature of a phase is the arrangement of the sites irrespective of the way they are occupied by the atoms. For some reason this particular γ configuration makes it a favourable one in a wide range of alloys.

6. The Hume-Rothery Law

A first step towards the understanding of alloy structures was made in 1926 by Hume-Rothery who pointed out that the electron-atom ratio is a main factor in determining the structure. The γ alloys afford one of the most striking instances. Typical formulae are Cu_5Zn_8, Cu_9Al_4, $Cu_{31}Sn_8$. Silver and gold may take the place of copper, and cadmium and mercury of zinc. It was shown by Ekman that there is also a γ series formed by the transition metals such as $(Fe, Co, Ni)_5Zn_{21}$, or Pd_5Zn_{21} and Pt_5Zn_{21}. In the first three types the ratio of valency electrons to atoms is 21 : 13 if copper is counted having one valency electron, zinc two, aluminium three, and tin, four. The other alloys also fall into line if the transition metals are reckoned to have no valency electrons. Similarly the β structure occurs for CuZn, Cu_3Al and Cu_5Sn in each of which the ratio is 3 : 2, and the hexagonal structure for ratios 7 : 4.

The law is only approximate, and there are many exceptions, but this is not surprising. Alloys are slowly annealed in order to attain equilibrium as nearly as possible, but adjustments of atomic position ceases before room temperature is attained and structures characteristic of higher temperatures are 'frozen in'. Ideally, one should test a rule of this kind by comparing the equilibrium structures at the absolute zero of temperature, where entropy plays no part and energy alone is the determining factor.

7. The Theory of Alloy Structures

An explanation of the Hume-Rothery Law involves the quantum theory. This is not the place to develop the theory in detail, which has such a strangely formal and unreal character when contrasted with the seemingly more natural and commonsense arguments of classical physics. Some indication may be given, however, of the way in which the peculiar features of metallic combination can be explained.

The alloy has been described earlier in this chapter as an assemblage of positive ions, combined with an interpenetrating sea of electrons which are held in common by all the metal ions. These 'free electrons' are supplied by the valency electrons of the neutral metal atoms. They are in rapid motion, interchanging places in the various atoms, forming a dynamic system that is often likened to the molecules in a gas. They drift along when the metal is conveying a current. They are vaporized off the surface, as it were, when the temperature is high (thermoelectric effect) or ejected when light of sufficiently high frequency falls on the surface (photoelectric effect).

To a first approximation, it is supposed that a definite amount of energy E is required to extract an electron from the metal surface. E is the 'binding energy' and in the photoelectric effect the energy of the light quantum $h\nu$ must be greater than E if it is to eject an electron. In other words ν must be greater than a critical frequency ν_0 given by $E = h\nu_0$.

This simple picture supposes that all the electrons are bound with the same energy E, but this is forbidden by the quantum theory which lays down that only two electrons in any one crystal can be in the same state. To interpret this rule one must define the 'states' by considering the electrons as waves, the wavelengths being defined by $\lambda = h/mv$ where mv is the momentum of the electron. It is this wavelength which accounts for phenomena of electron diffraction. In a rather artificial way, the electrons are considered as being standing waves in a rectangular box of the material like the fundamentals and overtones of a stretched string in a musical instrument. Each type of wave can accommodate two electrons.

If now one pictures adding electrons to the atomic structure until places are found for all the free electrons, the first pairs will go into the longest standing waves, representing the lowest values of energy, and then possible shorter wave modes will be filled up till all the electrons are accounted for. The binding energies of the electrons are spread out into a 'band' of levels. The conductivity of a metal can be understood in terms of this picture. It is always possible to add more electrons by using more of the higher levels, or to reduce their number by using fewer levels. Hence it is possible to increase the states with momenta in a particular direction; in other words, there is a flow of electricity.

The band of energy levels has a free surface. This is in contrast to the behaviour of a homopolar compound like diamond, or an ionic compound like NaCl. Here every place for an electron has an electron in it and so no electron flow can take place except by the process of lifting electrons out of their natural places into a quite new home of much higher energy. In this case the electrons are in a filled band; in a metal the band is un-filled. (One can swish water from side to side in a half-empty container, but not in one which is completely full.)

This picture of energy levels in the free-electron band ignores the influence on the energies of the atomic structure. The electrons, behaving like waves whose lengths is given by h/mv, are reflected by the planes of the crystalline arrangement when $\lambda = 2\,d\sin\theta$, like X-rays. Now it can be shown that waves falling on a set of planes which are just too long to be reflected by the planes have an abnormally low energy—less than one would expect from their wavelengths—whereas waves just too short have an abnormally high energy. The discontinuity in energy is greater for those planes that reflect more strongly.

This relation between the electron energies and the crystal planes explains the Hume-Rothery rule and the chemistry of intermetallic compounds. If the atomic arrangement in a phase has such a form that all the most energetic electrons have wavelengths that are just too long to be reflected by the strongest planes of the crystal, this phase will have a low energy and so is likely to appear in the equilibrium diagram.

The γ phase is a good illustration. Its strongest reflecting planes are (330) and (411) which have the same spacing of 2.08 Å since $(3^2+3^2+0^2)=(4^2+1^2+1^2)$. In order to accommodate 21 electrons to every 13 atoms, or 84 in the unit cell, one must use up states to a short-wave limit of twice this spacing—just right for near-normal reflection by the (330) and (411) planes. Hence, so to speak, the electrons can just be packed into low-energy states, and the γ structure is exceptionally stable.

The relation is shown formally in Fig. 7, which has some connection with the reciprocal lattice. The full line represents the energy of free electrons, which would be equal to $\frac{1}{2}mv^2$ or $p^2/2m$ where p is the momentum. Since $\lambda = h/p$ the curve relating energy and $1/\lambda$ is a parabola. In a crystal, however, this relationship is upset. If $1/\lambda$ is near to the vertical broken line, the parabolic relationship is no longer true; the energy just below is depressed and that just above is increased, and the curve is then shown by the dotted lines. This is the energy discontinuity just mentioned.

This treatment is only one-dimensional. In crystals, which are three-dimensional, the curves will be different in different directions; the basic curve for free electrons is the same, but the discontinuities occur at different places. It turns out that as the plane of the diagram (Fig. 7) is changed, the discontinuities trace out planes which are, in fact, parallel

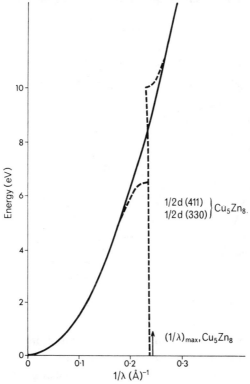

FIG. 7. Relationship between energy and wavelength of electrons in the crystal.

to the planes that cause the discontinuities by reflecting the electrons. There will of course, be several such planes, and they will form a closed shape known as a Brillouin zone.

We may approach the problem in a different way. Each electron has a momentum mv represented by a vector whose magnitude is proportional to $1/\lambda$. The point at the end of the vector represents the state of the electron. If the point lies on the surface of the Brillouin zone, the wave is reflected because sin θ. $1/\lambda = 1/2d$; any vector nearer the origin represents a wave too long to be reflected.

For the γ structure, the {411} and {330} planes enclose an almost spherical cage, as in Fig. 8, and all the electrons can be accommodated inside this cage on the low-energy side of the discontinuity.

It is now clear why a phase has a characteristic arrangement of atomic sites, whereas the way the atoms are distributed on these sites appears to be of secondary importance. It is the positions of the atoms,

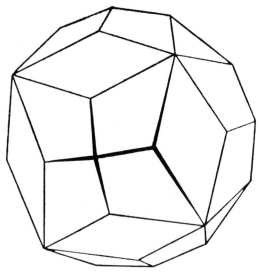

FIG. 8. The Brillouin zone for a γ-structure.

not their nature, which determine their cooperation in creating a strong reflection. To sum up, a 'phase' is characterized by a given number of electrons per atom, and an arrangement of atomic positions which brings the planes in the crystalline structure into the advantageous relationship with the electron waves.

8. Phase Diagrams

X-ray analysis by the powder method affords a powerful way of investigating the diagrams which show the phases formed when metals are mixed in different proportions. The classical way of studying such diagrams has been by the aid of polished and etched specimens, which show up the single-phase or two-phase character in mixtures of different proportions. X-ray analysis identifies the phases by their lines in the powder photograph and it has the further advantage that when more than one phase is present it reveals the composition of each phase. This is done by measuring the spacings of each phase which vary with the composition and so can be used as an index. The combination of phase identification and composition determination is very effective.

This is well illustrated by the study of ternary diagrams such as those in Fig. 9. The compositions are plotted by points in the triangle, with the three pure metals at the corners. Perpendiculars are drawn from a point to the three sides of the triangle, and the relative amount of metal, say Ni, is measured by the length of the perpendicular on the opposite side.

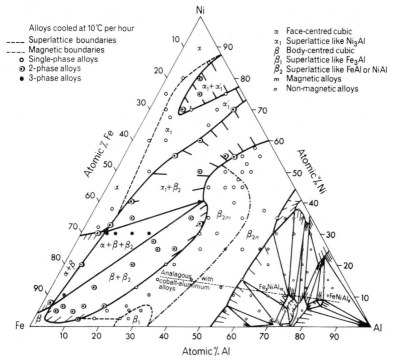

FIG. 9. Ternary phase diagram for the nickel-iron-aluminium system.

It was shown earlier in the chapter that the single-phase and two-phase region could be mapped out by picking a line rolling round the curves of Fig. 5. An analogous construction can be used for ternary diagrams. In this case the free energies are represented quantitatively by ordinates perpendicular to the triangle whose ends outline surfaces, and a plane is pictured as rolling over these surfaces. When it only touches one surface the region is single phase. If the plane rolls over two surfaces, the region is two phase with compositions represented by the two points of contact. When it is fixed in position by touching three surfaces, there is a three-phase region inside a triangle and the phases have compositions represented by the corners of the triangle. Since a plane touching three surfaces is fixed, the compositions of the three phases in equilibrium is also fixed, but in two-phase regions the compositions can vary.

9. Order-Disorder

Some alloys display a phenomenon which is an interesting and simple example of what is termed a 'phase change of the second kind', as distinct from a direct change of phase, that is of crystal structure, which is a 'phase change of the first kind'.

An alloy is a system in dynamic equilibrium. Atoms of different kinds are constantly being interchanged between one site and another, without destroying the crystalline structure, as is shown by the rapid interdiffusion of metals at temperatures well below the melting point. Although the process of interchange may have slowed down almost to a complete cessation at room temperatures, the alloy in cooling down after solidifying will at some time have passed through a temperature at which the process is rapid and its state will be characteristic of equilibrium at that temperature.

Some alloys can exist in a disordered state, in which the atoms of different kinds are distributed completely at random between all the sites or some particular set of sites of the phase pattern, or an ordered state where the atoms of each kind segregate to sites which form a regular pattern. The latter are called 'superlattices'. Thermal agitation, which causes the atoms constantly to change place, throws the alloy into the disordered state and this can usually be frozen in by quenching the alloy rapidly. If the alloy is slowly cooled by annealing, the ordering influence is able to assist itself as temperature movements decrease, and the ordered state is assumed. Tammann in 1919 suggested the existence of this ordering to explain the changes in electrical resistivity with heat treatment; the ordered alloy has a lower resistivity than the disordered alloy.

The existence of the ordering was observed by Johannson and Linde in 1925 by X-ray analysis of the alloy Cu_3Au. In the disordered alloy the sites of a face-centred cubic lattice are occupied at random by gold and copper, whereas in the ordered alloy the gold atoms segregate to the cube corners and the copper atoms occupy the remaining positions at face-centres. Bradley and Jay found a similar case in the alloy Fe_3Al which is body-centred cubic. The centres of the cubes have a random mixture of Fe and Al when disordered, and a segregation when ordered. The structures are shown in Fig. 10 and the X-ray evidence for the disorder is discussed in Chapter 16.

The course of the transformation can be followed by an approach due to Bragg and Williams; one pictures starting with an alloy in complete order at low temperatures and heating it. Energy is required to move an atom from an ordered site A into a disordered site B, because the former is the state of equilibrium. As the temperature is raised and the thermal agitation increases, a larger proportion of the atoms will on the average

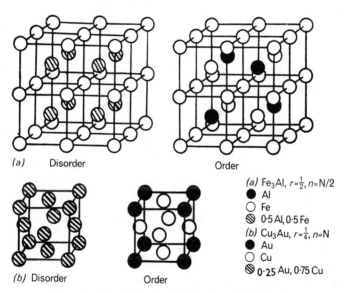

(a)   Disorder   Order

(b) Disorder   Order

(a) Fe_3Al, $r=\frac{1}{2}$, $n=N/2$
● Al
○ Fe
◉ 0·5 Al, 0·5 Fe
(b) Cu_3Au, $r=\frac{1}{4}$, $n=N$
● Au
○ Cu
◉ 0·25 Au, 0·75 Cu

FIG. 10. Disordering in (a) Fe_3Al and (b) Cu_3Au.

be in disordered sites. The degree of order of the structure can be measured in terms of the proportion of atoms 'p' in correct sites. For instance if there are equal numbers of atoms distributed on equivalent sites A and B in the structure, the degree of order S can be measured as $2p-1$. When all the atoms of one kind are on A sites, and all the others on B sites, $p = 1$ and therefore S = 1. When disorder is complete $p = 1/2$, because random distribution assigns to sites *A* or *B* one half of each kind of atom, and then S = 0.

If the energy required to interchange atoms on *A* and *B* sites were a constant V_0 for all degrees of order, then the curve of S plotted for convenience against kT/V_0 would follow a course as shown by the 'V constant' curve in Fig. 11. Disorder would continue to increase as the temperature is raised. This, however, will not be the case. The energy of interchange will depend on the degree of order; for instance if the degree of order drops to zero the energy of interchange will on the average be zero, because there is then no difference between an 'ordered' and a 'disordered' position. For simplicity let it be supposed that the energy V

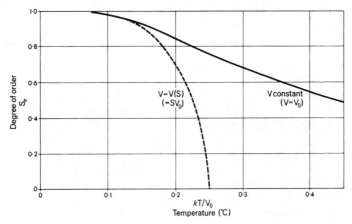

FIG. 11. Degree of order as a function of temperature.

is proportional to S ($V = SV_0$). As the temperature rises, not only will the thermal vibrations be more powerful, but also they will work against less opposition. The consequence is the dotted curve in Fig. 11. Disorder increases even more rapidly until at a certain critical temperature order disappears altogether. Calculation shows that this happens when kT/V_0 is equal to 0.25.

A social analogy may help to make the process clear. In a society in which most of the citizens are well-behaved and orderly, the difference between good behaviour and bad behaviour is clear. There is an ordering force which tends to make any one citizen conform to the accepted pattern. If, however, disturbing forces increase the number of neighbours who depart from good form, the ordering force on an individual decreases. 'If so and so is doing it, why should not I too?' Finally a critical point is reached when all distinction between right and wrong is confused and complete disintegration sets in.

Phase changes of the second kind. The characteristic of the order-disorder process is that although it can be counted as a change from one phase to another, it does not all occur at one temperature like for instance the change from solid to liquid or liquid to gas. The energy required to make the change is absorbed over a range of temperature and manifests itself as specific heat increased above the normal; it rises to a maximum and then falls to normal again above the critical temperature. This additional energy required to throw the alloy into disorder is equivalent to the latent heat in such cases as the melting of ice or boiling of water.

Examples of similar 'phase changes of the second kind' are found in many systems. For instance, the critical temperature is analogous to the Curie point in a ferro-magnetic like iron. At low temperatures the atomic magnets in iron have so strong a directing force on each other that they align themselves in groups or domains, inside each of which they all point in the same direction though different domains have different orientations. An external magnetic field swings round the polarity of the domains so that for the most part they point the same way and so the body is magnetized. As the iron is heated, temperature swings an increasing number of atomic magnets out of line with their neighbours (i.e. into 'disordered' positions) and so the ordering force on any one atomic magnet is decreased. The result is a rapid drop in ordering and finally a disappearance of all ordering in domains at the Curie point when the metal ceases to be ferromagnetic.

What is essentially a similar phenomenon occurs in the thermal expansion of quartz, which was examined by the X-ray powder method by Jay in 1933. The low-temperature form α quartz changes into the high-temperature form β quartz at 575°C; the relation between the two forms is shown in Fig. 12(*a*). As it were, kinks in the bonds of α straighten out in β. At low temperatures these kinks form a consistent picture (order), but as the temperature increases more and more are reversed in direction, until finally the ordering force vanishes and they all straighten out as in β. The curves for the expansion of quartz are shown in Fig. 12(*b*). There is an increasingly rapid extension as the kinks straighten out, followed by a nearly complete cessation of expansion above the critical point.

Short-range order. In 1935 H. Bethe introduced a new feature into the problem by showing that disorder does not become complete at the

β-Quartz, SiO₂   α-Quartz
                                  Trigonal

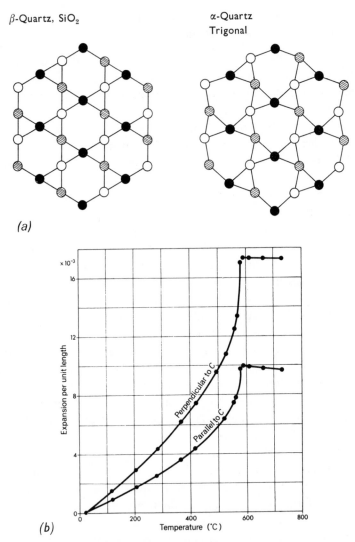

(a)

(b)

FIG. 12. (*a*) The relationship between α and β quartz with (*b*) variation of the thermal expansion of quartz with temperature.

critical temperature, but 'long-range order' changes into 'local order'. He considered a crystal of two kinds of atoms A and B in which, when ordered, A is surrounded by B atoms and B by A atoms.

By long-range order is meant a consistent scheme throughout the crystal whereby one set of sites is predominantly occupied by atoms of one kind. At the critical temperature this long-range order vanishes in the sense that in the whole crystal there are as many A atoms as B atoms on each site. However, owing to an ordered structure having a lower energy than a disordered one, small islands of partial order are continually forming and changing by atomic interchange, so that on the whole A is more likely to have an excess of B round it and vice versa. The Bragg and Williams curve is compared with the Bethe curve in Fig. 13.

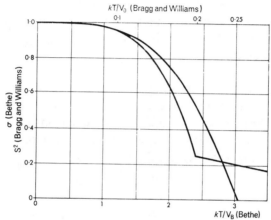

FIG. 13. Comparison of the Bragg and Williams and the Bethe theories of disordering.

That this must be the case may be seen by considering the entropy of the system. For a given energy, which in this case means a given number of wrong neighbours, entropy will be greatest for the most probable way of arranging these wrong neighbours because this gives the lowest free energy. If the number of wrong neighbours is few, the most probable distribution is to have a coherent system of A and B sites throughout the crystal and have the 'wrong' atoms randomly distributed amongst them. It would be very improbable to have two separate portions of the crystal in one of which A is right and the other B is right, because one would have to use up all one's 'wrong' in creating the interface where one system changes into the other. As the number of 'wrongs' increases, however, they become so numerous that a consistent scheme for A or B right through the crystal is very improbable. In this case the local order has the lowest free energy. The free energy curves for long-range and local order cross at the critical temperature, and the structure leaves the one and proceeds along the other.

The simplicity of the order-disorder change and the ease with which the changes can be pictured make it an excellent practical example of entropy principles. For instance Boltzmann's law states that an entropy difference where one system changes into another is measured by $k \log w$, where w is the relative number of possible arrangements in the two cases. If an ordered binary alloy with n atoms changes into a disordered one, there is only one way to have complete order, and 2^n ways to arrange atoms anyhow. So the entropy difference should be $k \log_e 2^n = nk \log_e 2 = R \log_e 2$ where R is the gas constant. $R \log_e 2 = 1.38$ cal. per g atom per °C, and measurements in β-brass give 1.01 cal per g atom per °C, a quite good agreement.

Resistivity and specific heat. Ideally, the resistance of a pure metal is proportional to the temperature, approaching zero as the temperature falls towards the absolute zero. In terms of the quantum theory, resistance is due to the scattering of the waves representing the electrons. At absolute zero this scattering ceases because the metal is quite uniform, and behaves

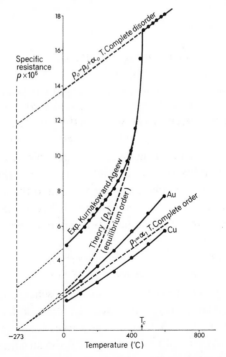

Fig. 14. Variation of resistivity with temperature.

like a body of perfect transparency. At higher temperatures the thermal motions cause variations from uniformity which scatter the electrons, and transparency changes to increasing turbidity as the temperature rises.

An alloy in which order is perfect might be expected to behave like a pure metal, with a resistivity αT proportional to the temperature. On the other hand disorder should have the same effect as temperature, causing irregularities which scatter the electron waves, and a given state of disorder will add a constant value ϱ_d to the resistivity ϱ so that $\varrho = \varrho_d + \alpha T$.

As the alloy cools from a point above the critical temperature, it would be expected to follow a line tending to the value ϱ_d at absolute zero, where ϱ_d is the part of the resisitivity due to complete disorder. At the crucial temperature there will be a sudden drop due to the onset of order, and as order becomes complete the curve should tend to follow the line $\varrho = \alpha T$.

Figure 14 shows measurements (1931) made by Kurnakow and Ageew. Their upper curve was for cooling in 3 hours, the lower one for cooling in 12 hours. This form is of the type to be expected, but clearly complete order was not attained with these rates of cooling; the curve to be expected for equilibrium is shown by the dotted line. There is similarly a discontinuity in the specific heat at the critical temperature.

10. Permanent Magnets

The first permanent magnets were made of hardened steel. They had a very low retentivity, or power of retaining their magnetism when an opposite field tended to demagnetize them, and so the magnets were very weak. The alloys now used for permanent magnets are quite extraordinarily more powerful with a factor of merit some hundred times as great. The parent of these strong magnets was an alloy of iron, nickel, and aluminium, discovered by Nishima in 1931, with the approximate formula Fe_2NiAl.

Bradley in 1937 tried to find the reason for this highly favourable magnetic behaviour by investigating the ternary system iron–nickel–aluminium. Other people had taken X-ray powder photographs of Fe_2NiAl but could deduce little from them. Bradley decided that it would be more fruitful to examine alloys of many different compositions, and produced a complete diagram for the ternary system; his interpretation of the iron–nickel rich part of the diagram is shown in Fig. 15.

There are only two types of phase in this part of the diagram—the α type which is face-centred like nickel and the β type which is body-

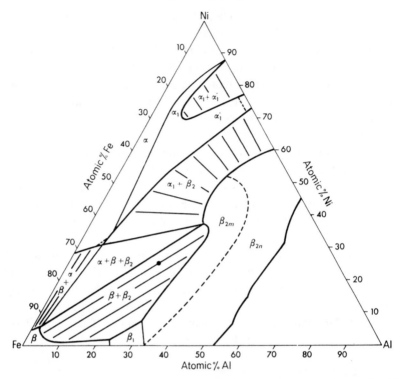

Fig. 15. Bradley's interpretation of the iron-nickel rich part of the NiFeAl phase diagram.

centred like iron—but there are many secondary differences of structure, depending on the way the atoms are distributed between the sites, which need not be gone into here. The part of the area which is of interest for the magnetic properties is the region marked $\beta + \beta_2$, Nishima's alloy being indicated by the black dot. It is in a kind of bay in the extensive β area, so that when an alloy in this region breaks down into two phases, as indicated by the lines, they are both very similar phases though of different composition. The β phase is almost pure iron; the β_2 phase is a region whose iron or nickel is predominantly at cube corners and aluminium at cube centres.

If the alloy is rapidly cooled, the distribution of iron, aluminium and nickel on the lattice points is random (Fig. 16(*a*)). If slowly annealed, it forms a two-phase structure with separate regions of β and β_2 (Fig. 16(*b*)). In neither case are the magnetic properties of special interest.

The strong permanent magnets are produced by an intermediate rate of cooling, and Bradley deduced that in this case there is a segregation into iron-rich and iron-poor regions as in Fig. 16(c) but no break-down into separate phases. As the iron-rich regions are forced to conform to the larger dimensions of the parent lattice they are expanded in a state of

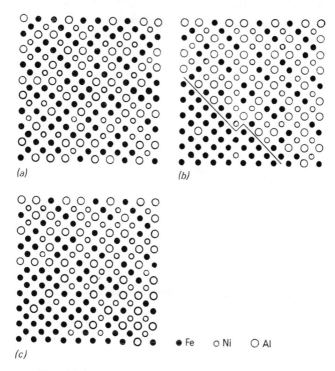

● Fe   o Ni   ○ Al

FIG. 16. Structures of iron-aluminium-nickel alloys.

immense strain and this is believed to be the cause of the remarkable magnetic properties.

Strain and magnetism are related by the effect called magnetostriction. A ferromagnetic alters its dimensions when placed in a magnetic field, shrinking or expanding parallel to the field with a converse expansion or shrinking at right angles to it. Conversely if the material is in a state of strain, it favours the magnetization which would produce such a strain. The magnetization is pinned down in a particular direction and is prevented from changing to another direction, so giving the ferromagnetic a high retentivity.

It was found that the addition of cobalt further increased the retentivity because it increased the magnetostriction, and that it could be still further increased in a favoured direction by cooling the material down in a strong magnetic field. Earlier types of hard steel magnets had to be made in an elongated shape to reduce the demagnetizing influence of their own poles. Modern magnets have so high a retentivity that they can be short and chunky, and so lend themselves to a variety of technical applications.

CHAPTER 15

MACROMOLECULES

1. Proteins

The determination of protein structure has marked a most dramatic turning point in X-ray analysis. The molecules are so complex that, almost up to the point when success was finally attained, it seemed an impossible dream to think it could be done. Now that the way has been found, the number of protein structures which have been analysed is growing apace.

The proteins are organic molecules of very high molecular weight which form the structure of living bodies. Each molecule is made to a pattern determined by the genetic material in the cell. Broadly speaking they are of two types, the fibrous proteins and the globular proteins. The fibrous proteins are used to provide the structural framework of the body. Examples are the keratins of skin and hair, horn and nail, and the collagen in sinews. These fibrous proteins are chemically inert and, because of the complex ways in which the individual molecules aggregate, they do not crystallize though they often show some degree of organization.

The globular proteins, on the other hand, often exist as individual molecules with a definite structure and form highly perfect crystals. Each has a definite chemical function to perform. Whereas the fibrous proteins may be likened to the materials which build the walls, roof, floors, and windows of the factory of a living body, the globular proteins are the machines installed in it. The enzymes are organic catalysts tailored to bring about one specific chemical reaction. There are hormones like insulin, or carriers and storers like haemoglobin which transports oxygen and myoglobin which stores it in the muscles. The chemical action is generally very simple, but the complex structure of the protein ensures that it is brought about at the right place and in the right way. The proteins vary widely in size, but even the simplest ones have molecular weights in the ten to twenty thousand range, and more complex molecules may have molecular weights measured in millions. The proteins have a very ancient origin; many which developed in primitive forms of life because they were useful for a certain function have been handed down during the ages as higher forms of life developed. For instance the haemoglobin in mammalian blood is closely similar to that in an insect larva. The number of proteins required for all the tasks in a living cell is very large; a unicellular organism employs thousands of different species and a higher form of life may have millions.

The peculiar nature of protein is summed up in Perutz's introduction to *The Structure and Action of Proteins* by Dickerson and Geis:

> 'To understand the chemical basis of life we must know the machinery that builds up complex plants and animals from simple chemical precursors. What kind of apparatus is it that living cells employ to make large organic molecules in an aqueous medium, at ambient temperatures and in neutral solution, when chemists setting about the same task would employ powerful solvents, high temperatures, low pressures, and strong acids or bases? The answer lies in the efficient catalysts used by living cells to speed up reactions which would normally proceed imperceptibly slowly, ten or even a hundred thousand times. In order to accomplish this, cells provide a special catalyst for each small metabolic step.'

Although only such a small fraction of the protein species have been examined so far, the way in which they perform their task is becoming clear because of the knowledge of their actual structure which has been provided by X-ray analysis.

2. The Chemical Structure of Proteins

One can picture two possible ways in which a large molecule designed to perform a specific function in the body might have been developed. Each protein might be something of its own kind, specially designed as a complex structure and bearing little relation to other proteins. On the other hand each might be made of simple units of a limited number of types and the complexity could then be introduced by the order and arrangement of these units. We might compare the alternatives with the two ways in which writing has been developed in the East and West. The Chinese use a very large number of characters, each of which stands for some basic concept. The Western writing is based on an alphabet with a relatively small number of letters, and the many different words are formed by the order in which their letters are placed.

Nature has adopted the second alternative. The proteins are polymers built of twenty kinds of quite simple units, the amino acids, listed in Table 1.

TABLE 1

The Amino-acids: $NH_2.C_\alpha H(R).COOH$

Non-polar		*Polar*	
Name	*R*	*Name*	*R*
Glycine (Gly)	$-H$	Serine (Ser)	$-CH_2OH$
Alanine (Ala)	$-CH_3$	Threonine (Thr)	$-CH(OH).CH_3.$
Valine (Val)	$-CH(CH_3)_2.$	Asparagine (Asn)	$-CH_2.CONH_2.$
Leucine (Leu)	$-CH_2.CH(CH_3)_2$	Glutamine (Gln)	$-CH_2.CH_2CONH_2.$
Isoleucine (Ile)	$-CH(C_2H_5).CH_3$		
Phenylalanine (Phe)	$-CH_2.C_6H_5.$	Tyrosine (Tyr)	$-CH_2.C_6H_4.OH$

Tryptophan (Trp)

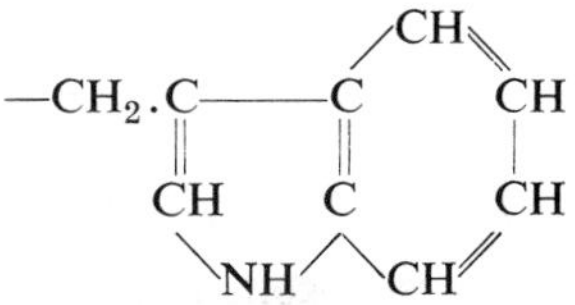

Cysteine (Cys)	$-CH_2.SH$		
Methionine (Met)	$-CH_2.CH_2.S$ [.CH_3.$	Aspartic Acid (Asp)	$-CH_2.COOH$
		Glutamic Acid (Glu)	$-CH_2.CH_2.COOH$
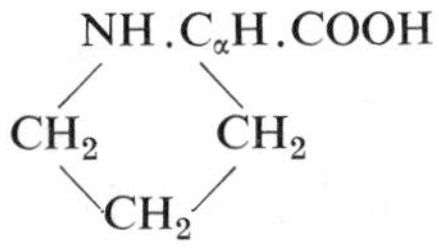 Proline (Pro)		Lysine (Lys)	$-CH_2.CH_2.CH_2.CH_2$ [.NH_2.$

an *imino acid* with R group linked also to N:

Arginine (Arg) $-CH_2.CH_2.CH_2.NH$ [.C(NH)NH_2.$

Histidine (His) $-CH_2.C=\!=\!=CH$

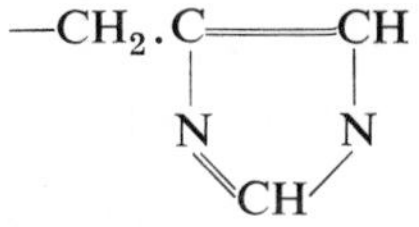

Each amino acid has a central α carbon atom with four bonds. Three of these bonds are formed in an identical way in them all—to a hydrogen atom, an amino group, and a carboxyl group. The group attached to the fourth bond is different for each and characterizes the amino acid. In the process of polymerization the amino group of one acid links to the carboxyl group of the next, by the elimination of water, so producing a peptide chain as shown in Fig. 1. A protein molecule consists of one or more of these chains with a characteristic succession of amino-acid residues. The chains are linear, never branched, and typical chains contain 150–300 amino-acid residues. Lengths of chain may be connected by links such as disulphide bridges formed by cystine. In addition to these chains some proteins contain a few special atoms, such as iron or zinc, which play an essential part in their function.

The amino-acid residues R in Fig. 1 differ in chemical character, being neutral, basic, acidic or hydrogen-bond forming. They are hydrophobic or hydrophilic. They may be likened to the components of these

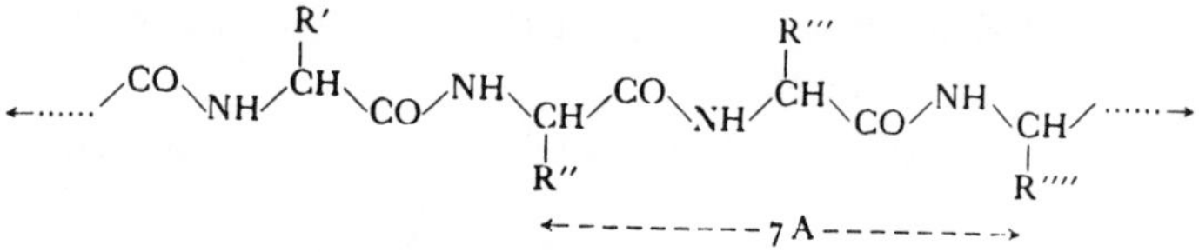

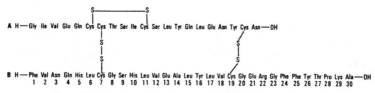

FIG. 1. The chemical structure of proteins.

construction kits for young people which have parts of a few standard kinds, together with some special items of cogs and wheels (the zinc or iron), which can be bolted together, to construct complex engineering structures and machines. The protein is tailored to perform its function by arranging suitable units in a suitable conformation.

Sanger in 1952 made the first determination of the order of the amino acid residues in a protein, insulin (Fig. 2)—a success for which he was awarded a Nobel Prize. There are two chains of 21 and 30 residues;

A H—Gly Ile Val Glu Gln Cys Cys Thr Ser Ile Cys Ser Leu Tyr Gln Leu Glu Asn Tyr Cys Asn—OH

B H—Phe Val Asn Gln His Leu Cys Gly Ser His Leu Val Glu Ala Leu Tyr Leu Val Cys Gly Glu Arg Gly Phe Phe Tyr Thr Pro Lys Ala—OH
    1   2   3   4   5   6   7   8   9   10 11 12 13 14 15 16 17 18 19 20 21 22 23 24 25 26 27 28 29 30

FIG. 2. The amino-acid sequence of insulin.

they are bound by two disulphide bonds and a third bond of this kind binds two parts of the upper chain together. As so commonly happens, once a way of getting the sequence had been discovered many ways of shortening the labour were developed and the determination of a sequence is now much more straightforward though still a challenging process.

With the exception of the simplest member, glycine, the amino acids are optically active and have the laevo form. It is interesting to reflect that this must have started purely by chance. If the whole living world were reflected in a mirror, as in *Alice through the Looking Glass* it would work equally well. As it is, the laevo forms are interdependent. A laevo animal can only manufacture or assimilate other laevo forms of life.

3. Protein Crystals

The globular proteins crystallize readily, but the first attempts to get X-ray diffraction pictures of them failed. The reason for this was discovered by Bernal, who was successful in getting diffraction pictures by making exposures with crystals in their mother-liquor. If removed from the liquor, they collapse into internal disorder. The perfection is well shown by diffraction pictures such as that of lysozyme (see Chapter 11, Fig. 7) taken with a Buerger precession camera.

The diffracted beams become weak and fade out at a spacing which varies from one protein to another, but is generally in the region of 1.5 Å. This corresponds to a resolution like that shown in Fig. 11. It is not quite sufficient to separate atoms clearly but the general shape of molecules is outlined and the electron-density map can be interpreted if additional information about the probable identity is available, such as that provided by a known sequence of amino acids.

When I came to the Cavendish Laboratory in Cambridge in 1938, M. F. Perutz who was then a young research student had obtained very fine diffraction pictures of the protein haemoglobin, which showed that in principle enough information was available to solve the structure if only a way of deciphering it could be found. These pictures so fired our imagination that we embarked on investigations to analyse the crystal. The most complicated molecules hitherto analysed had contained less than a hundred atoms, whereas the number in haemoglobin was about 12 000 —and when using classical methods the difficulty of analysis went up as quite a high power of the number of atoms. Though it was known that the molecule consisted of polypeptide chains, with four haem groups, nothing was known about the way in which the chains were arranged and any trial-and-error method of checking the position of the atoms by guessing was completely out of the question. Many of our colleagues made no secret of their opinion that we were attempting the impossible!

The investigations continued for twenty-five years before they finally led to success. Some definite information about the haemoglobin molecule was gleaned, such as its external shape, but in the main it was a story of exploring avenues which turned out to be blind. We were lured on because we expected the polypeptide chains to be arranged in an organized regular way inside the molecule, for instance as a bundle of parallel rods. There were indications, we believed, of such a stacking in the Patterson diagrams of the molecule, and our hopes were based on discovering the structure and arrangement of the rods which should show up in the Patterson synthesis if they were parallel. As it finally turned out, this assumption was false; the chains are actually in most complicated convolutions. I think if we had realized their complexity we might well have abandoned the investigation as hopeless. The solution finally came through a discovery made by Perutz, which will be described in a later section.

4. The Pauling-Corey α-Helix

Another line of attack on the structure of polypeptides had been going on for a long time before crystal investigations started. Astbury made pioneer X-ray diffraction studies of the fibrous proteins such as the keratin of hair and wool. His X-ray pictures of these materials (see section 9) had shown that the chains could exist in a stretched form (β-keratin) or a folded form (α-keratin). In the former the chain is extended to its fullest length, with a repeat of about 3.4 Å in accord with the CO—CH—NH bond lengths. In the latter the chain shrinks by folding to about half this length. Astbury showed that there is some feature of the folded chain which gives a repeat of the structure at every 5.1 Å, and he estimated that there are about three amino-acid residues per repeat. It had also been deduced that the chains are held in the contracted form by hydrogen bonds between CO and NH groups in adjacent folds, and that these bonds are roughly parallel to the general chain direction.

Astbury proposed a kind of Greek key pattern for the folded chain, but it seemed more probable that the real form was some kind of helix, because this gave every amino acid a similar site in the structure. Ideas about the form of the folded chain were very vague, however, till in 1951 Pauling and Corey established its structure in an elegant and convincing way in their famous paper on the 'α-Helix'.

The key to their solution was the realization that, on chemical grounds, the adjacent groups CO and NH are coplanar. It follows that all the bonds, from one α carbon through CO and NH to the next α carbon, are in one plane. The only place where a corner can be turned in folding the chain is at the α carbon itself where rotation can take place about the single bonds. (Fig. 3)

This restriction defines the α-helix, shown in Fig. 4, as a stable form of folded chain. The pitch of the screw is about 5.4 Å, and the amino acids repeat at distances parallel to the helix of 1.5 Å, roughly corresponding to Astbury's estimates. The hydrogen bonds between successive turns

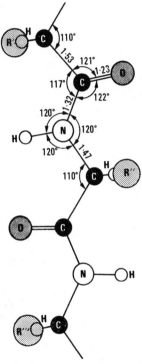

FIG. 3. The planar arrangement of atoms around a peptide bond.

are approximately parallel to the helix axis. A feature which is so obviously possible when pointed out, but which had been overlooked by crystallographers obsessed with regular symmetry, is that the number of amino-acid units per turn is not integral, being about 3.6.

Perutz confirmed the existence of the amino-acid repeat at 1.51 Å. Cochran, Crick and Vand worked out the theory of diffraction by structures with helical symmetry, and showed that the diffraction pictures given by poly-benzyl L-glutamate are in agreement with the α helix struc-

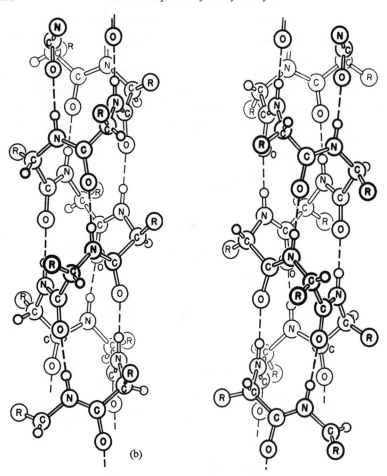

Fɪɢ. 4. Right and left-handed α helices. The side chains (R) on the α-carbon atoms are in the position corresponding to the known configuration of L-amino acids in proteins. (From a drawing by Professors L. Pauling and R. B. Corey.)

ture. Subsequently, Crick showed that α-keratin is made of α-helices arranged in coiled coils and everything fell into place: the fundamental molecular structure of α-keratin was completely confirmed.

At first it seemed probable that the Pauling-Corey helix might lead to the solution of globular protein structures, which at that time were still thought likely to be regular assemblages of polypeptide folded chains. But now that a number of structures has been analysed, it has turned out that the α-helix is not an essential feature of a protein molecule, though a common one. Some molecules have a large proportion of their amino acids in α-helices, others have little or none. However, myoglobin, the first protein to be analysed, is one of those with a large α-helix content and the recognition of its existence in almost exactly the predicted form was an important factor in confirming that the solution was on the right lines.

5. Phase Determination with Heavy Atom Derivatives

The key to the analysis of protein molecules was discovered by Perutz in 1953. He showed that a complex containing a heavy atom could be attached to a specific point in a molecule, that there were measurable differences between the diffraction by crystals of the native protein and those in which heavy atoms had been attached, and that the phases of the $F(hkl)$ values could be reliably deduced from these differences.

The first success in using the heavy-atom method only led to a very partial solution which told little about the structure, but it will be described in some detail because it was a turning point in protein analysis; it showed that the heavy-atom method 'worked'. It is also an interesting example of X-ray optics.

Perutz's investigations had been concentrated on haemoglobin which has a molecular weight of 64 500. This substance transports oxygen from the lungs to all parts of the body, and carries away the waste product carbon dioxide. Each molecule contains four haem groups which are planar structures of four linked rings with an iron atom at the centre, and it is to this iron atom that the oxygen molecule is attached.

The molecules form monoclinic crystals with twofold symmetry axes. Perutz had found that the unit cell had a variety of forms, depending on the ambient conditions. The axes a and b remain constant in length, but the length of c and the monoclinic angle β vary as shown in Fig. 5(*b*) where one is looking down the b axis. It was clear that the structure of the (001) layers, the projections of which are seen vertically in Fig. 5(*a*), is constant in all the forms, which differ only in the relative displacement of these layers by their sliding over each other to different extents.

Figure 5(*c*) compares the reciprocal lattice arrangement of the (*hol*) diffracted spots for all these forms. Since the a axis remains constant, all spots lie on the same lines parallel to c^* but, owing to the variation of β and c, the spots lie at different points on these lines.

Perutz measured the diffracted spots for the different cells, and all the results were plotted on the reciprocal lattice lines of the one diagram.

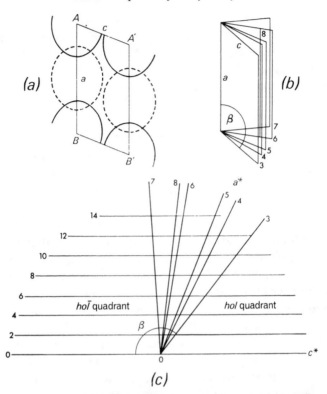

FIG. 5. (a) arrangement of molecules in the normal wet unit cell of horse met-haemoglobin. (b) swelling and shrinkage stages. (c) relation of transform to stages shown in (b).

Four lines are shown in Fig. 6. Since there is a twofold axis parallel to b, the phase angles are O or π and the values of F, being necessarily either positive or negative, were therefore drawn above and below the line.

All the signs are of course unknown, but one can see that there must be relations between them in this figure. The values of F in the composite diagram are all due to diffraction by the molecules in the same orientation, so one is sampling the molecular transforms at various points along the reciprocal lattice lines. The transform will be positive in certain areas, negative in others, with boundary lines between $+$ and $-$ areas where it is zero, so a sample along a line has nodes and loops like the vibrations in a string. The values in a loop must be of the same sign, whereas the sign changes when passing through a zero value (node) into the next loop.

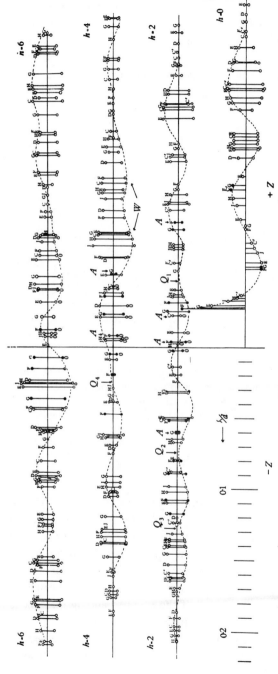

Fig. 6. Salt-free structure amplitudes of *hOl* reflections from crystals of horse met-haemoglobin at different lattice stages. The broken curve gives the correct signs and is derived in combination with the isomorphous replacement method. The layer lines are separated by an arbitrary distance. Letters refer to the lattices observed in different shrinkage stages.

It was hoped that these sign relationships might make it possible to fix signs for the spots, but no way was found to relate the signs in one line with constant h to those in another until the position was dramatically altered by taking into account the effects of introducing heavy atoms. The effect on the F values of attaching a para-mercuribenzoate unit is shown in Fig. 7. Owing to the twofold axis which passes through

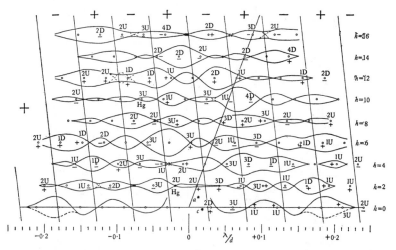

FIG. 7. Waves of the haemoglobin transform. Doubtful nodes are marked by broken lines. The points correspond to the reciprocal lattice of the normal wet crystals. Their markings denote the observed changes in amplitude due to a mercury-benzoate residue; U or D stands for up or down. The oblique straight lines denote the nodes between the fringes due to diffraction by a pair of mercury atoms at $X = 0.068$, $Z = 0.290$ and $X = -0.068$, $Z = -0.290$.

The signs of the fringes are indicated at the top of the diagram.

each molecule, the mercury atoms are in pairs. The diffraction by a pair of atoms gives a set of fringes, alternately positive and negative. The positions of the mercury atoms could be found by a Fourier method, as described in an earlier chapter, and the fringes they form are shown in Fig. 7. as + and − areas across the pattern, in a direction perpendicular to the line joining the mercury atoms. The signs of the protein F values can now be read by inspection. If the effect of adding mercury is to increase (U for up) the F value in a positive fringe area, the F value must be positive. If it decreases (D for down), the F value must be negative. The effect in a negative fringe area is of course the opposite. Inspection of

Fig. 7. shows that in every case the U and D effects agree in giving signs to the loops in a consistent way.

When the signs are known, it is possible to construct a Fourier synthesis of the electron density in the molecules projected along the b axis (Fig. 8). Very little information can be gleaned from this projection, because the molecule is about 53 Å thick and so many atoms are super-

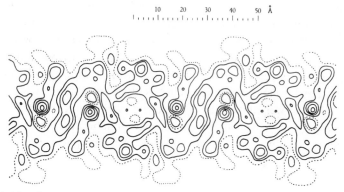

FIG. 8. Fourier map of the electron density in haemoglobin projected along the b axis.

imposed. It is clear that a three-dimensional analysis is essential for interpretation of the structure.

The solution was an important milestone, however, because it was so convincing a proof that reliability could be placed on the use of heavy-atom derivatives. In general the addition of one heavy-atom is not sufficient to fix phases; several such atoms in different sites are needed, but in this special case the determination of the nodes and loops made the results quite definite.

6. The First Protein Analysis; Myoglobin

Haemoglobin, on which so much effort had been spent, was not the first protein to be solved. In order to get a three-dimensional electron-density map it is necessary to know the general phases for a large number of values of $F(hkl)$. Ideally two heavy-atom additives in different sites should give the phase without ambiguity, but actually two are barely sufficient because in so many cases it will happen that owing to interference the contribution by a heavy atom to values of $F(hkl)$ is small, and so is not significant. For comprehensive phase determination at least three additives are required and four or five are desirable for confirmation.

Perutz at first only found it possible to get one additive for haemoglobin, and although this was enough to solve the (010) projection because of the peculiarly favourable range of forms, as already described, it was not enough to give a three-dimensional map.

The first structure to be solved was that of myoglobin, by Kendrew. Myoglobin has a molecular weight of 17 500 and consists of a single chain of 153 residues. It contains one haem group, and its function is to store oxygen in the muscles so that it is available for action. It is particularly abundant in mammals and birds which dive for long periods and so need an abundant oxygen reservoir. Kendrew worked with myoglobin from the sperm-whale and seal myoglobin has also been studied by Scouloudi. The molecular weight is about one quarter that of haemoglobin.

Myoglobin proved to be particularly suitable for the heavy-atom method; Kendrew was able to make seven isomorphous replacements

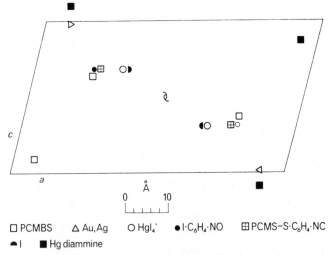

FIG. 9. Positions of heavy atom substitution in the unit cell of sperm-whale myoglobin.

with the atoms in the positions shown in Fig. 9. His analysis was carried out in three stages, first to a resolution of 6 Å in 1957, then to 2 Å in 1959, and finally to 1.4 Å in 1962, this last being the limit at which diffracted beams faded out.

The analysis to 6 Å required phase determination for some 400 reflections. I well remember the excitement of this first analysis. The Davy–Faraday Laboratory of the Royal Institution joined forces with Kendrew in Cambridge in making the necessary measurements, for at that time even four hundred reflections, for the native protein and each of the isomorphous replacements, seemed quite a heavy task. While this was going on I had access to the figures, and I was able to satisfy myself that for some thirty or forty sample reflections with general phases it was possible to calculate with sufficient accuracy both the positions of the additives and the phases (by drawing the vector diagrams). This was not a part of the main attack, which was carried out systematically by Kendrew in Cambridge for all the reflections. It was a thrilling time for me person-

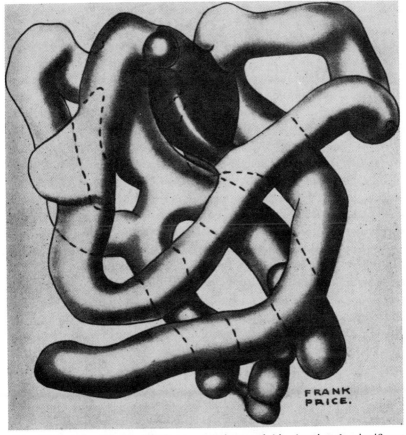

FIG. 10. Drawing of a model of sperm whale myoglobin showing the significant electron density at a resolution of 6 Å.

ally, however, because it showed that the goal had at last been reached, after all the years of struggle and that a new chapter in the story of X-ray analysis had been started. I well remember the occasion when Kendrew brought me the 6 Å model which he had just made from the Fourier map, and our marvelling at its intricacy. The model is shown in Fig. 10. At 6 Å resolution one can only see the general masses of atoms. The course of the chain can be followed; it consists of rods which later proved to be portions of an α helix, linked somewhat ambiguously by slender portions of extended chain. The haem group shows as a disc of extra density.

The subsequent story of the extension to higher resolution is well illustrated by Fig. 11 which is a superposition of contoured levels in the 1.4 Å Fourier synthesis. The main object of interest is the haem group which is seen edge-on near the middle of the diagram. The iron atom at the centre is linked to a histidine above right which is part of a chain, and below the haem, closely linked to the iron, is an atom which in this case is a water molecule, but shows where the oxygen molecule would be attached. It seems amazing that all the Fourier elements should combine to show the position of a single atom in a complex of 1260 atoms not counting hydrogen, and it is a striking witness to the accuracy of phase and amplitude determination.

The peculiar conformation of the myoglobin chain is no accident. Perutz was later able to analyse haemoglobin, and found that it consists of four chains in almost exactly the same conformation as myoglobin. Haemoglobin is in fact like four myoglobin units stuck together to form a spheroidal molecule. The twining of the chain in these units must in some way provide the necessary housing for a haem group.

The amount of computation involved in working out a structure like this is fantastic; it could not possibly be done without a digital computer. If one wishes to pass from one resolution to another twice as good, the number of spots to be measured is increased eightfold. While some 400 reflections sufficed for the 6 Ångstrom map, 10 000 were needed for 2 Ångstrom resolution and 25 000 for 1.4 Å. To take the case of the 2 Å representation, some 10 000 diffractions must be measured for the native protein and for each isomorphous substitution. For each value of *hkl*, the *F* values of native and substituted molecules must be put into an equation to determine phase (10 000 equations). The amplitudes and phases are put into a three-dimensional Fourier series with 10 000 terms, and this series is summed as 100 000 points in the unit cell. Contours passing through equal values are then drawn on sections. For the 1.4

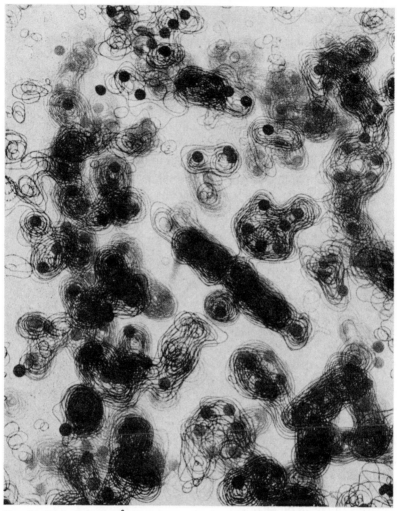

FIG. 11. Part of the 1.4 Å. Fourier synthesis. Centre, the haem group (edge-on), showing haem-linked and distal histidines, and water molecule attached to the iron atom. Bottom right, a helix end-on. Left, a helix seen longitudinally, together with several side chains.

Ångstrom resolution the Fourier synthesis was summed at half-a-million points in the unit cell.

In practice automatic methods which greatly shorten the labour are now available for handling the measurements, but the task still remains formidable.

7. Lysozyme

It is not possible to give other than a very brief description of protein structures in this chapter. So many structural details in each of the vast molecules are of interest that it would be possible to write a book about any one of them. (An excellent review will be found in *The Structure and Action of Proteins* by Dickerson and Geis.)

However, the structure of lysozyme may be conveniently described in some detail because it is such a good example of enzyme action. Lysozyme was the next protein ofter myoglobin to be worked out, by Phillips and his colleagues at the Royal Institution. Enzymes are catalysts and each one controls the rate of a particular chemical reaction. In 1894 Emil

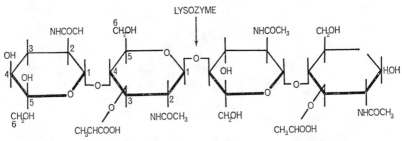

FIG. 12. The cell-wall tetrasaccharide with the β-(1—4) glycosidic linkage hydrolysed by lysozyme shown by an arrow. The formula is drawn in a way that is now unconventional to resemble more closely the actual atomic arrangement.

Fischer suggested that an enzyme has such a specific action because it has a shape which precisely fits the substrate to which it attaches itself in performing its catalytic action. He likened it to the way in which a key fits its lock. The structure of lysozyme established by Phillips completely confirms Fischer's prediction.

Lysozyme is an enzyme widely distributed in living bodies which kills invading bacteria by dissolving their cell walls. These walls are formed of chains of sugar rings similar to those in cellulose, which are then joined side-to-side by short lengths of polypeptide chain. It is a structure like that of the fabric corduroy, the polysaccharide chains being the ribs. The enzyme acts by severing these chains. A portion of chain is shown in Fig. 12 and the point where it is cut is marked.

Phillips and his co-workers analysed lysozyme by the methods which had been successful for myoglobin. They then found out where it attached itself to the substrate. This was done by adding an inhibitor, a kind of small stopper molecule which is so like a portion of the substrate that it becomes attached to the active site of the enzyme and stops its functioning. It is rather like a burglar giving the watchdog a piece of meat so that it will not bite him. They used as inhibitors di- or tri-saccharides, and found where they joined on to the lysozyme molecule by calculating Fourier maps of the changes in electron density from the changes in *F* values that were observed when the inhibitors were added.

The substrate fits into a cleft in the lysozyme structure (Fig. 13). It is held in place in the cleft by hydrogen bonds between bond-forming

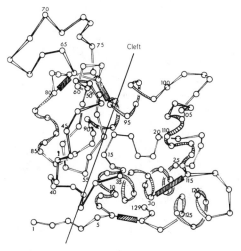

FIG. 13. The course of the main polypeptide chain in lysozyme (drawing by the author).

atoms of the amino acid residues that came into place exactly opposite bond-forming atoms of the substrate. The point in the chain where the cut is to be made then comes exactly into place opposite two active residues, aspartic acid and glutamic acid, which catalyse the action. Figure 14 shows the structure with the substrate in place.

8. Protein Architecture

Each protein molecule is fitted to perform a highly specific chemical task by an arrangement of amino acid residues with the necessary chemical character in the necessary positions. This is brought about by the sequence of amino-acid residues in the chain or chains, and the folding of

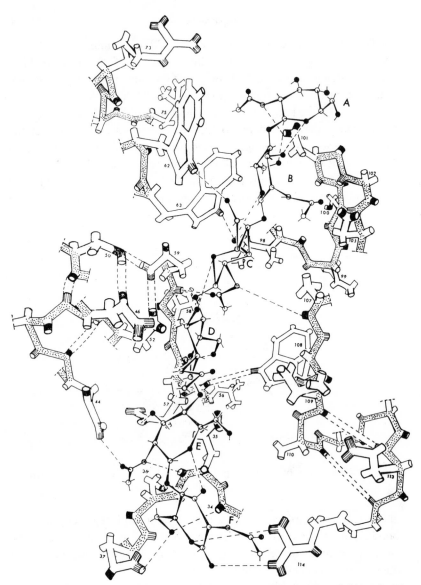

FIG. 14. Atomic arrangement in the lysozyme molecule in the neighbourhood of the cleft with a molecule of hexa-N-acetylchitohexanose shown bound to the enzyme. The polypeptide chain is shown speckled and NH and O atoms are indicated by line and full-shading respectively. Sugar residues A, B, C are observed in the binding of tri-N-acetylchitotriose (and β-N-acetylglucosamine for residue C). Residues D, E, F occupy positions that have been inferred from model building. It is suggested that the linkage hydrolysed by the action of the enzyme is between residues D and E.

the chain which determines their juxtaposition. Chemical properties and conformation are both essential. A molecule such as that of lysozyme is like a complex machine tool for making some special part, with clamps to hold the work in the right place (the hydrogen bonds) so as to bring the cutting tools (the active residues) into just the right position to perform their task. In general the hydrophilic residues are on the outside of the molecule and the hydrophobic residues are inside. Water molecules are highly polar, and tend to cancel out the effect of electrically charged units by clustering round and shielding them. It appears that the nonpolar hydrophobic part of the molecule may serve a function of allowing the electrical charges to exhibit their influence, because in contrast to water the hydrophobic units have a low dielectric constant. Other residues may just be packing to support the active part of the molecule in the right conformation.

Proteins have a very ancient origin as has already been stressed; they are common over wide ranges of living matter from the simplest organisations to the highest. Proteins which must have had a common origin, because they have such similar chain conformations, may differ considerably in their amino-acid content, and the further apart they are in the tree of life, the greater are the differences. In this way they provide a clue to the stages at which various forms of life branched off from each other. It would seem that in many places in the chains residues can be replaced by others without changing the function of the protein, but there are certain residues which are invariable as if they were vital and irreplaceable.

There is such a wealth of information in the structure of any one protein that although so few of the vast total number have been analysed, they already present an *embarras de richesse* in studying how their detailed structure determines their function.

As an instance of the advance in the power X-ray analysis over the last fifty years, the frontispiece to this volume shows the structure of a haemoglobin molecule with, for comparison, the unit of pattern of sodium chloride, NaCl.

9. Helical Structures

When a polymer is formed by the joining together in a string of a number of units which have identical types of bonding, the result is inevitably a helical structure. The second element is in a definite orientation compared with the first, the third element has the same orientation with respect to the second, and so they follow each other in a helix like a

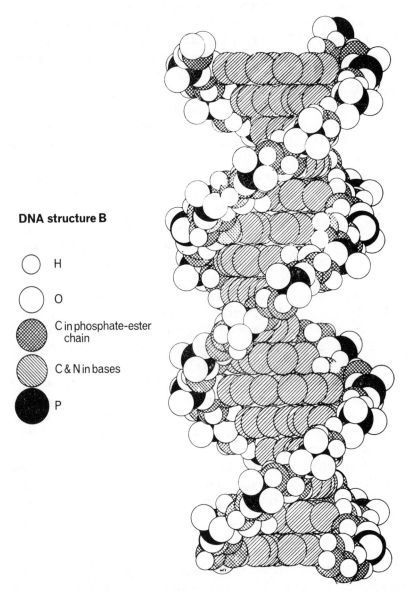

DNA structure B

○ H

○ O

◍ C in phosphate-ester chain

◍ C & N in bases

● P

FIG. 15. The double helical structure of deoxyribose nucleic acid (DNA).

corkscrew or spring. An example is Pauling's α-helix which has already been described. It is the basis of keratin, the substance of feather, hair, horn and skin. Another example is collagen, the fibrous protein which is used for parts of the body which have to stand up to tension, like the tendons. The arrangement is just like that of a rope, three left-handed coils of extended polypeptide chain being wound together into a right-handed twist. The most famous of such special structures is the 'Double

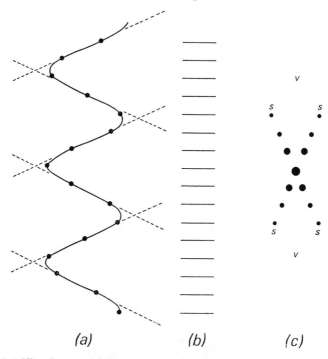

(a)   *(b)*   *(c)*

FIG. 16. Diffraction by a helical structure. (*a*) distribution of monomer units on the helix as projected on a plane (*b*) separation of scattering units on planes perpendicular to the helix axis (*c*) schematic of diffraction pattern showing spectra *S* arising from 'reflection' from adjacent turns on the helix (broken lines) and *V* arising from 'reflection' from planes (*b*) perpendicular to the helix axis.

Helix' of the gene material DNA (Fig. 15) for the discovery of which Crick, Watson and Wilkins were awarded the Nobel Prize.

It cannot be claimed that these structures were primarily discovered by X-ray analysis, like the proteins. They were inferred from their chemical compositions and functions, and by stereo-chemical reasoning. The fibrous proteins do not crystallize, though they may have a degree of ordered arrangement, and X-ray photographs show only a relatively small number of diffuse reflections. The X-ray results in the main can only be used to confirm and to add detail.

An element of helical structure is shown in Fig. 16(*a*). The positions of the units are determined by the pitch and radius of the curve on which they lie, and by the translation from one to the next along the axis. There is of course no necessary relation between this translation and the distance parallel to the axes between successive turns of the screw, its pitch, as was first pointed out by Pauling in the case of the α-helix.

The diffraction pattern of such a helical arrangement is complex. It was first analysed by Crick, Cochran and Vand in a series of Bessel functions, and they used their theory to prove that α keratin was indeed composed of α-helices as Pauling had inferred.

There are features of the diffraction, however, which follow in a simpler way from the nature of a helix and which can be very apparent in a diffraction picture. First, the turns of the helix in Fig. 16(*a*) are like

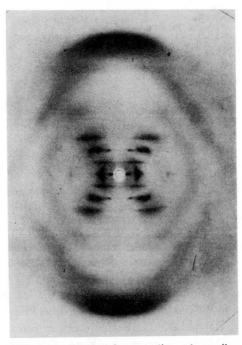

FIG. 17. X-ray diffraction pattern from sodium deoxyribose nucleic acid, structure B.

the lines of two inclined diffraction gratings. Each grating produces a series of orders marked S in Fig. 16(c), and together they form an X-shaped figure. The slope of the arms of the X, together with the spacing of the spots along them, give the pitch of the helix and its radius. Second, the units from which the helix is made repeat at distances shown by the horizontal series of lines in Fig. 16(b), and the waves from this spacing give a first-order spot in the vertical axis of Fig. 16(c), marked by V, whose distance from the origin gives the spacing of the units along the helix axis. The picture is of course more complex when each repeating unit contains many atoms each on its own helix, and there are also diffraction effects due to the packing together of the helices, but if some part of the repeating unit is a predominantly strong scatterer the corresponding X may stand out in the diffraction pattern. This is the case in DNA. Each helix is formed of alternate phosphate and sugar groups, and the intertwining pair of helices are linked sideways by bases termed purines and pyrimidines. The phosphorus atoms, which are shown as black circles (Fig. 15), are exceptionally dense and produce the X structure shown in Fig. 17.

Analysis of the structures of proteins and of the genetic material has triggered off an explosion of research into the function of these constituents of living matter. The familiar story is being repeated: X-ray analysis finds how atoms are arranged, and this knowledge provides an essential basis for further work.

CHAPTER 16

IMPERFECT CRYSTALLIZATION

1. The Sharpness of Spectral Lines

When a line-grating forms optical spectra, a line in the spectrum is not perfectly sharp even if the light which forms it can be regarded as strictly monochromatic. Its breadth depends on the number of lines in the grating. The light is diffracted most strongly when $n\lambda = a \sin \theta$ exactly, where a is the spacing of the grating, but for a small range of angle on either side of θ, the wavelets are nearly in phase and add to form an appreciable resultant. This resultant falls to zero at angles $\theta \pm \delta\theta$, where $\delta\theta$ is such that the wavelet from the middle of the grating is in opposite phase to those from each end. If there are 100 000 lines $\delta\theta/\theta$ is of the order 1/100 000, and to resolve a spectral doublet on which the lines are 1/100 000 of a wavelength apart, we must use a grating with at least 100 000 lines.

To sum up, the greater the number of lines in a grating, the sharper are the spectra, the easier it is to resolve lines which have nearly the same wavelength, and the greater is the precision with which wavelength can be measured.

2. Diffraction by Small Crystals

The same principle holds for X-ray diffraction. If the regular sequence of reflecting planes extends over a large number of planes, the angle at which diffraction takes place is sharply defined. If on the other hand the sequence is a short one, due to irregular crystallization or diffraction by extremely small crystals, then the diffracted beam will be diffuse. A measurement of its width tells us how small the crystallites are.

Because crystals are three-dimensional, however, the effects from them are more complicated than for a one-dimensional grating; each dimension has to be considered separately. Suppose that a crystal is large in two dimensions and is small in the third. Then the angular variation mentioned in section 1 is appreciable only for this third dimension. If the short direction is parallel to the *c* edge of the unit cell, we can say that there is a spread in the index *l*. Thus the X-ray reflections are elongated into short lines, and from the length of these lines the thickness of the crystal can be deduced.

If the crystal is needle-shaped—that is, it is short in two dimensions, say *b* and *c*—then the reflections spread in both *k* and *l*. In other words, they now form plates. If the crystal is limited in all directions, then the X-ray reflections are also diffuse in all three indices, and the sizes of the crystallites can be deduced.

In practice, of course, conditions are not so simple. It is unlikely that a small crystal will be spherical, and the shape may not be simply related to the crystallographic axes. Nevertheless, the broadening of X-ray reflections can give a good idea of how small the crystals in a powder specimen are, and the method has been used to determine the average size of particles in materials such as colloidal gold, where the dimension may be of the order of 100 Å.

3. Diffraction by Deformed Crystals

A small crystal is perfect over a definite volume. If a specimen consists of a large number of small crystallites, the positions of the atoms in each crystallite are perfectly related to each other, but there is no relation between the atoms in neighbouring crystallites. But if a large crystal is deformed in some way, a different situation exists; if one atom is taken as defining the origin of the crystal, the further we move from this position the less definitely do we know the positions of the atoms we come to. Again, there is a finite volume over which the crystal can be considered perfect, but it is not ideally perfect within this volume and there is still some relation between the atoms within the volume and outside it. This state of affairs exists when we deform a metal by stretching or twisting it.

It might be thought that the overall effect would be the same as for small crystals, but this is not so because the definite boundary of the small crystallite has disappeared. What do we take as the boundary? We may take it as the place where the atoms scatter out of phase (see section 1) with that at the centre. But this criterion will be different for different orders of diffraction, for a change of phase α for a first order will become 2α for the second order. Thus the particle size deduced from the second order would be half that from the first. In fact no absolute answer would exist.

We may look at the problem in another way. For small particles there is an increase in the breadth of the X-ray reflections with angle simply because a variation in $\sin \theta$ in the equation, $n\lambda = 2d \sin \theta$, gives a bigger variation in θ as θ approaches 90°. For deformation, an additional effect is introduced; since, as we have shown, for higher orders the deformed crystals behave as though they were smaller, the variation of line broadening with θ is even greater than it is for small crystals.

The two relationships can be easily worked out, and it may sound a simple matter to distinguish between them. In fact it is not; the distinction is greatest at small angles, where the broadening, because it is relatively small, is most difficult to measure. The problem is important in practice because the solution is needed in our understanding of the behaviour of metals when they are cold-worked, and in the 1930s there was some vigorous discussion between two opposing schools. One said that cold work broke up the crystallites into much smaller ones; the other said that the main effect was the deformation that has just been mentioned.

Now, with more precise means of measurement, it has been found that both effects exist, but that distortion is the more prominent. But it is not surprising that, since both effects are difficult to deal with theoretically the combination of the two together presented in the 1930s a very formidable problem.

4. Irregular Stacking of Layers

In principle, all crystals should be perfect because perfection leads to minimum free energy. But if some of the forces between the atoms in a crystal are weak, they may not make much contribution to the free energy and thus the structural features that depend upon them may not be perfectly regular. The most marked example of this type of occurrence is shown by graphite, a form of the element carbon.

The perfect structure of graphite is shown in Chapter 13, Figure 3. It has layers of carbon atoms strongly joined together, the distances between them being 1.42 Å; the layers however are 3.30 Å apart. The structure accounts for the 'flaky' properties of the material, since it is easily possible for the layers to move over each other. In the extreme case the layers may have no relation to each other in orientation and atomic positioning and yet retain parallelism and regular spacing. Such a structure shows sharp reflections from these planes, but no other reflections at all. It is called 'turbostratic'. This is an extreme case; many sorts of arrangement exist with varying degrees of regularity. Always the reflections from the atomic planes are sharp, but the others have varying degrees of diffuseness.

A still more interesting structure is shown by the element cobalt. Elements should have one structure at one temperature, although that structure can suddenly transform to another one if the temperature is changed. Cobalt is an exception; most specimens contain a mixture of face-centred cubic and hexagonal close-packed crystals (Chapter 14, section 3), and the hexagonal part—but not the cubic—shows an intriguing mixture of sharp and diffuse lines. Why cobalt should behave in this way is a mystery, when all the other elements are so well behaved; nevertheless, the structure that gives this pattern is quite well understood.

It arises because both the cubic and hexagonal structures can be considered as made of layers, but, unlike graphite, the forces between the layers are as strong as those within them. In each layer the centres of the atoms lie on the corners of an equilateral network, marked (1) in Fig. 1(a). The next layer of spheres whose centres are marked (2) fit

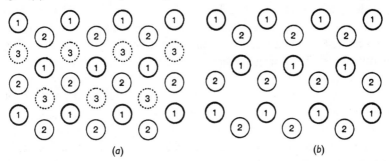

(a)   (b)

Fig. 1. The superposition of layers in the two forms of closest packing (a) cubic (b) hexagonal.

over (1) if each sphere is over the centre of the triangle below. In adding the next layer there are two alternatives; it may be put directly over (1) as in Fig. 1(b) or in the position (3) shown in Fig. 1(a). Fig. 1(a) represents the cubic close-packed arrangement; Fig. 1(b) is the hexagonal close-packed arrangement.

It is perhaps not surprising that the hexagonal form of cobalt should occasionally 'forget' which sequence it is using, and insert a layer (3) when it should be using only (1) and (2). If it uses (3) it then continues to use (2) and (3) or (1) and (3) and will go on until it 'forgets' again. A typical perfect sequence is about 10–20 layers, although, of course, it varies from specimen to specimen.

How does one recognize such a structure from its diffraction pattern? It can be regarded as a structure based upon a perfect lattice with a small unit cell in which some of the atoms are missing. This small unit cell is hexagonal with a equal to the distance between neighbouring sites—(1), (2) and (3)—in Fig. 1(a) and c equal to the distance between layers. As far as this unit cell is concerned the atoms are all in correct positions, and all the reflections from it are sharp. But all the other reflections are diffuse. Since the layers are perfect however, the diffuseness is similar to that given by thin plate-like crystals (section 2); that is, the reflections are extended in the direction corresponding to the l index. It is in this way that the interesting diffraction pattern containing sharp lines and diffuse lines of various widths is produced.

5. Irregular Arrangement of Atoms in a Perfect Lattice

There is a similar phenomenon in connection with the alloy Cu_3Au, which also can show a mixture of sharp and diffuse lines. Fig. 2 shows powder photographs of this alloy which, as explained in Chapter 14 on metals, exhibits the order-disorder change. The atoms, which are on a face-centred cubic lattice, occupy these positions quite at random at high temperatures. The corresponding powder diagram on the right therefore shows only the reflections due to a cubic face-centred lattice with indices all even or all odd, such as 111, 200, 220, 311, etc. As the alloy cools, the gold atoms segregate to the corners of the cube, leaving the face-centres to the copper atoms. (See Chapter 14, Fig. 10.) Since the gold atoms are heavier than the copper atoms and are on a simple cubic lattice, they produce all the reflections characteristic of such a lattice, as seen by the indexed lines of the fully-ordered structure on the left of the diagram, with no restrictions as to indices. As the new lines are due to the difference in scattering power of gold and copper they are weak compared with the lines of the face-centred lattice, where gold and copper effects add.

The ordering that sets in first extends over small regions in the structure, with no consistency between one region and the next. As ordering increases, the regions become bigger until finally there is one scheme of order for the whole crystal. This process can be seen clearly in the photographs. In the second from the right, the lines due to the gold atoms going to corners are weak and diffuse. In the third from the right the

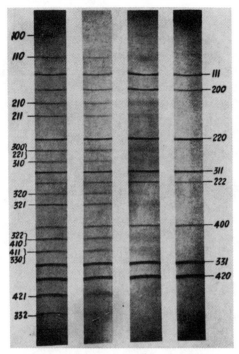

FIG. 2. Powder photographs of the alloy Cu$_3$Au in various stages of disorder.

order is still too local to resolve the $K\alpha$ doublets at the end of the film (e.g. 332, 421). In the final film on the left, ordering is complete over large regions and these doublets are resolved. The face-centred lines due to the combination of Cu and Au of course remain sharp throughout.

6. Forms of Imperfection

Imperfection can be of many types. Two intriguing examples will be given below to illustrate the way in which X-ray analysis can be used to determine its nature.

Imidazole Met-haemoglobin. Figure 3 is a photograph of the *h0l* reflections of this crystal, in which an imidazole molecule has been attached to the haem groups; it shows some very interesting features. Some layer lines have sharp spots; in others they are drawn out into diffuse streaks along the layer line. The structure only permits even values of h, and the sequence runs: $h = 0$, sharp; 2, very diffuse; 4, moderately sharp;

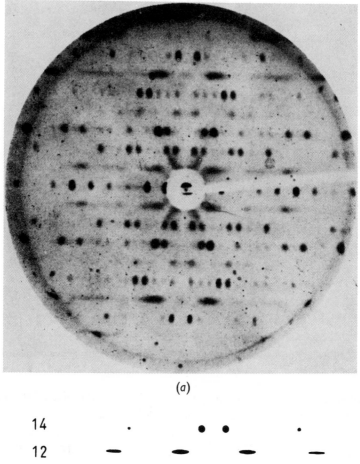

(a)

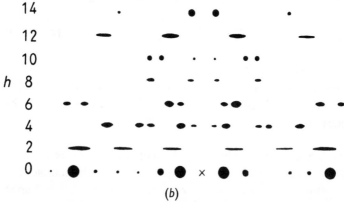

(b)

FIG. 3. (a) precession photograph and (b) diagrammatic representation of the strength and diffuseness of the *hol* reflections from imidazole met-haemoglobin.

6, moderately sharp; 8, diffuse; 10, sharp; 12, very diffuse. At the twelfth layer line the sequence repeats as if there was a mirror plane there, i.e. 14 is sharp and 16 diffuse, and the same sequence repeating at the twenty-fourth and thirty-sixth layer lines can be traced out to the thirty-eighth.

The *a* and *b* axes of the crystal are identical with those of normal monoclinic haemoglobin (Fig. 4(*a*)) in which the C-face is centred as described in Chapter 15 (page 223). The *c*-layers are obviously tough structures because they remain unchanged in numerous forms of haemoglobin which only differ in the way these layers are stacked on each other (compare section 4). However, in the crystals containing imidazole the reflections *hol* are symmetrical about both the vertical and horizontal axes in Fig. 3, as if the crystal had orthorhombic symmetry. In order to account for the symmetry, layers with the molecules inclining to the right,

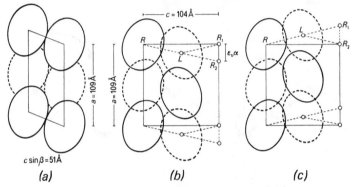

FIG. 4. (*a*) monoclinic horse met-haemoglobin.
(*b*, *c*) relative displacements of C-sheets of molecules in imidazole met-haemoglobin.

the '*R*' layers, must alternate with '*L*' layers in which they incline to the left as in Fig. 4(*b*). The *L* layers fit onto the *R* layers as shown in this figure, with a small downward displacement. It is however also possible to fit *L* onto *R* with a similar slight upward displacement as in Fig. 4(*c*). The one arrangement is related to the other by a vertical twofold axis parallel to *a*, so they are identical.

When the next *R* layer is fitted onto *L* it may either continue the downward movement, so that the centre of the molecule is at R_2, or it may go up to R_1 which is level with *R*. (Fig. 4(*b*)). Similarly if *L* has first gone up, it may continue to go up to R_1 or go down to R_2. (Fig. 4(*c*)). The sequence of sharpness or diffuseness is explained by assuming that the planes move up or down completely at random. When the next *R* plane is fitted onto the *L* plane in Fig. 4 there is an even chance whether it goes up or down. It cannot, as it were, 'sense' where the first *R* level is through such a thickness of *L*. The displacements may be 'up, up' 'up, down', 'down, up' or 'down, down' so that there is only a 50–50 chance that the centre of the molecule will come back to the level position. If of course it always did so the structure would be a regular orthorhombic one and all the spots would be sharp. It is actually 'statistically orthorhombic'.

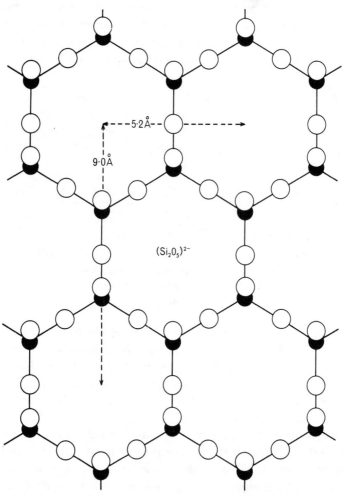

FIG. 5. The hexagonal type of silicon-oxygen sheet.

The displacement R_1R_2 throws the molecules in that layer out of phase with those in the R layer and the phase irregularities between clusters of sheets causes the diffuseness. The rule for the extent of the diffuseness is as follows:—If the displacement is a fraction ε_0 of $a(R_1R_2 = \varepsilon_0 a)$ then the h layer line will be sharp if $h\varepsilon_0$ is nearly an integer, and diffuse if it departs widely from an integer.

When $h\varepsilon_0$, which measures the path difference in wavelengths, is nearly an integer the displacement only introduces a small phase difference. The integral part can be neglected because it introduces a whole number of wavelengths in the path difference; it is only the remainder which matters. In going to layers further and further away from the layer R, the random ups and downs lead to an increasing divergence in phase, but if each jump introduces only a small difference it will be only after many layers that they mount up to so much that all coherence with the starting point is lost. The diffraction will therefore be like that produced by crystallites of relatively large size and the spots will be sharp. On the other hand if $h\varepsilon_0$ is far from being an integer, all coherence is soon lost, and the spots will have the diffuseness characteristic of very small crystallites.

The sequence of sharpness and diffuseness is accounted for by assuming $\varepsilon_0 = 0.208$. For instance the second layer line is diffuse because $2\varepsilon_0 = 0.42$, i.e. the displacement introduces nearly a path difference of $a/2$ which is as bad as it could be. The tenth layer line is sharp because $10\varepsilon_0$ is 2.08, close to an integer. The zero layer line is of course sharp, because the displacement makes no path difference. The following table reviews the whole series, the figures for ε in the last column representing the departure of $h\varepsilon_0$ from a whole number.

h	reflection	$h\varepsilon_0$	ε
0	sharp	0	0
2	very diffuse	0.42	0.42
4	moderately sharp	0.83	0.17
6	moderately sharp	1.25	0.25
8	diffuse	1.67	0.33
10	sharp	2.08	0.08
12	very diffuse	2.50	0.50
14	sharp	2.92	0.08
16	diffuse	3.33	0.33

These correspondences, which continue to hold up to the thirty-eighth layer line, may be compared with Fig. 3.

Chrysotile Asbestos. Asbestos is an extremely fibrous mineral. One form of asbestos is an amphibole and the fibres are naturally explained as being parallel to the strong silicon-oxygen chains in that mineral. The fibrous nature of chrysotile asbestos, however, arises in quite a different way. In structure it is one of the lamellar minerals like mica or clay, based on 'wire-netting' like silicon-oxygen sheets as shown in Fig. 5.

A bundle of chrysotile asbestos fibres gives the diffraction photograph shown in Fig. 6. However small the specimen it always gives a diffraction picture like that of a complete rotation photograph. Some

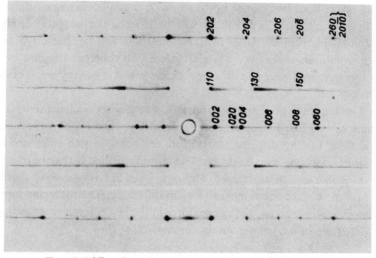

FIG. 6. Diffraction photograph of clinochrysotile asbestos.

spots are sharp, others have a 'flare' extending outwards from the spot along the layer line, like a comet with its tail.

The explanation lies in the extreme tendency, first pointed out by Pauling, for the lamellae to curl up into tight rolls. The sheets in mica show no such tendency, because each sheet is composed of two silicon-oxygen layers, with the vertices of the tetrahedra pointing towards each other (Fig. 7) and held together by aluminium or magnesium atoms, so both sides of the mica sheets are the same. However, the sheets o chrysotile have a silicon-oxygen network on one side, and a structure like magnesium hydroxide on the other. If the mica sheet is compared to a sandwich, the crysotile sheet is a slice of bread with butter on only one side. The dimensions of the magnesium hydroxide structure are nearly the same as those of the silicon-oxygen network to which it fits, but not exactly so, hence there is a tension which causes the curling.

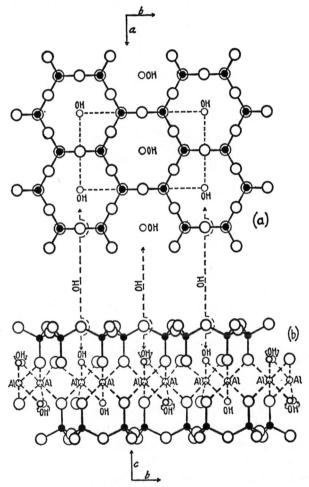

FIG. 7. Portions of the mica structure.
(a) a single layer of the hexagonal network of silicon oxygen tetrahedra with hydroxyl ions located in the plane of their vertices and the centres of every sixfold ring.
(b) an edge-on view of two of these layers with inward pointing vertices showing their relative orientations and the locations of the Al atoms between them.

The effect of the curling is illustrated by Figure 8. The fibres are parallel to the *a*-axis of the structure, and whatever their length the sheets can remain in register in the *a* direction. This is presumably why they grow to such a great length in this direction. Because of the curling, however, they cannot keep in register in the *b* direction, and the way they fit onto each other in this direction must be completely random.

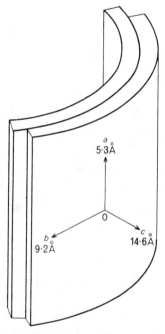

FIG. 8. Diagram showing the relationship of the unit cell axes of chrysotile to the curved layers of the structure.

As regards that part of the roll on which the X-rays fall tangentially, in the direction *Ob* the random displacement parallel to *b* does not affect the *hol* spectra which are therefore sharp spots, such as would be produced by a regular three-dimensional crystal. Such spots will be seen on the second layer line in Fig. 6. Since the *a* axis appears to be halved in the tangential projection, there are none of these spots in the first and other odd layer lines.

The part of the roll on which the rays fall normally, in the *cO* direction, behaves like a set of superimposed two-dimensional gratings because there is no phase relationship between one sheet and the next.

Plane gratings are formed by the silicon-oxygen framework sheets with axes 5.3 Å and 9.2 Å (Fig. 8), and give *hk* spectra. If such a grating were everywhere normal to the X-rays, it would give sharp spots. Owing to the curvature, however, there is an effect like that observed when one tilts an optical line grating, which makes the spectra move to higher angles because the spacing of the grating is effectively less. The *hko* flares on the first layer line have a head due to the diffraction when the X-rays fall normally in the direction *Oc*, and spread towards higher angles as the tilt increases on either side.

This interpretation of the diffraction effects is supported by the electron micrograph shown in Fig. 9. The rolls of the synthetic chrysotile are short, but in the natural product they are of immense length compared with their diameter, because growth can continue indefinitely in the *a* direction.

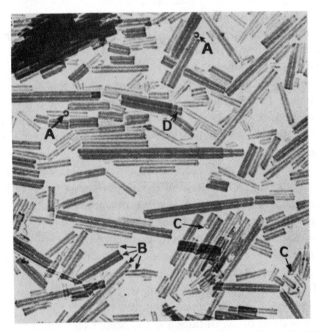

FIG. 9. An electron micrograph of synthetic chrysotile (×78 000)
A. end on view of the tubular fibres.
B. the hollow channels in fibres of varying diameter.
C. fibres with obliquely broken ends.
D. fibres fitting one to another in telescopic arrangement (photographed by W. Noll).

These examples show the kind of information which can be got from the form of the reciprocal-lattice spots. Any departure from sharpness indicates a corresponding departure from perfect crystal symmetry.

7. The future

Imperfect crystallization is common and it is clear, from the few examples given in this chapter, that our understanding of the subject is still limited. So far, we have been able to give a more-or-less complete explanation of only a few types. As the complication of the disordering increases, the problem of interpreting the diffraction patterns becomes doubly difficult, not only because of the complication itself but also because the evidence available becomes less. When we come to the very imperfect structures, such as those of the natural substances that were discussed briefly in Chapter 15—hair, muscle, teeth, etc.—or the synthetic high polymers, X-ray photographs seem to show very little detail indeed. Yet the information is there and we must try to interpret it.

There are immense difficulties. But the X-ray crystallographer has always been faced with immense difficulties. In the 1920s the first X-ray photographs of the silicates seemed unbelievably complex, and the task of interpreting them impossible; yet we now know that they were relatively simple. In the 1930s the first photographs of the protein crystals were daunting; the number of spots was so large there seemed no hope of finding atomic coordinates from them. Yet the problem was faced resolutely, even though the necessary facilities for a complete solution did not exist. As the work progressed, new procedures came into play. The automatic diffractometer and the digital computer were invented, and new contributions, such as the use of anomalous scattering, were made. Thirty years later success was achieved.

The examination of imperfectly crystallized materials poses similar challenges now. The difficulties appear insuperable. But a start has been made and some of the simpler problems, as we have shown, have been successfully solved. There is no reason why in, say, fifty years' time the understanding of even the most obdurate structures should not be as complete as those of the silicates and the proteins are now.

BIBLIOGRAPHY

Chapter 1   1. *Fifty Years of X-ray Diffraction*, P. P. Ewald (ed.) *and numerous crystallographers* (1962) for Int. Union of Crystallography by Oosthock's Uitgerersmaatschappij, Utrecht.

2. *X-rays in Theory and Experiment*, A. H. Compton & S. K. Allison (1935), D. Van Nostrand, Princeton, N. J.

Chapter 2   3. *Early Papers on Diffraction of X-rays and Crystals*, J. M. Bijvoet, W. G. Burgers & G. Hägg (eds.) *Vol. I* (1969): *Vol. II* (1972), for Int. Union of Crystallography by Oosthock's Uitgerersmaatschappij, Utrecht.

Chapters 3   *The Life and Letters of an English Physicist, 1887—1915*, H. G. J.
and 4.   Moseley & J. L. Heilbron (1974), Univ. of California Press, Berkeley, Los Angeles & London.

5. *Spectroscopy of X-rays*, M. Siegbahn (1924), Oxford University Press, London.

Chapter 5   6. *The Crystalline State. Vol. 1. A General Survey*, W. L. Bragg (1949), G. Bell, London.

Chapter 6   7. *Introduction to Crystallography*, F. C. Phillips (1963), Longmans Green, London.

8. *International Tables for X-ray Crystallography, Vol. I* (1952), International Union of Crystallography: Kynoch Press, Birmingham.

Chapter 7   9. *The Crystalline State Vol. II. The Optical Principles of the Diffraction of X-rays*, R. W. James (1948), G. Bell, London.

Chapters 8   10. *The Crystalline State. Vol. III. The Determination of Crystal Struc-*
and 9   *tures*, H. Lipson & W. Cochran (1953), G. Bell, London.

Chapter 10   11. *Optical Transforms*, C. A. Taylor & H. Lipson (1964), G. Bell, London.

Chapter 11   12. *The Interpretation of X-ray Diffraction Photographs*, N. F. M. Henry, H. Lipson & W. A. Wooster (1961), Macmillan, London.

13. *Single-Crystal Diffractometry*, U. W. Arndt & B. T. M. Willis (1966), Cambridge University Press.

Chapter 12   14. *The Crystalline State Vol. IV. Crystal Structures of Minerals*, W. L. Bragg & G. F. Claringbull (1965), G. Bell, London.

15. *Structural Inorganic Chemistry*, A. F. Wells (1950), Oxford University Press, London.

Chapter 13 16. *Organic Crystals and Molecules*, J. M. Robertson (1953), Cornell University Press, Ithaca.

Chapter 14 17. *Atomic Theory for Students of Metallurgy*, W. Hume-Rothery (1952), The Institute of Metals, London.

18. *Introduction to Solid State Physics*, C. Kittel (1966), J. Wiley, New York.

Chapter 15 19. *The Use of X-ray Diffraction in the Study of Protein and Nucleic Acid Structure*, K. C. Holmes & D. M. Blow (1966), Interscience, New York.

20. *The Structure and Action of Proteins*, R. E. Dickerson & I. Geis (1969), Harper & Row, New York.

Chapter 16 21. *X-ray Optics*, A. J. C. Wilson (1962), Methuen, London.

22. *X-ray Diffraction*, A. Guinier (1963), W. H. Freeman, San Francisco & London.

INDEX

A CATALOG OF SELECTED
DOVER BOOKS
IN SCIENCE AND MATHEMATICS

A CATALOG OF SELECTED
DOVER BOOKS
IN SCIENCE AND MATHEMATICS

QUALITATIVE THEORY OF DIFFERENTIAL EQUATIONS, V.V. Nemytskii and V.V. Stepanov. Classic graduate-level text by two prominent Soviet mathematicians covers classical differential equations as well as topological dynamics and ergodic theory. Bibliographies. 523pp. 5⅜ × 8½. 65954-2 Pa. $10.95

MATRICES AND LINEAR ALGEBRA, Hans Schneider and George Phillip Barker. Basic textbook covers theory of matrices and its applications to systems of linear equations and related topics such as determinants, eigenvalues and differential equations. Numerous exercises. 432pp. 5⅜ × 8½. 66014-1 Pa. $9.95

QUANTUM THEORY, David Bohm. This advanced undergraduate-level text presents the quantum theory in terms of qualitative and imaginative concepts, followed by specific applications worked out in mathematical detail. Preface. Index. 655pp. 5⅜ × 8½. 65969-0 Pa. $13.95

ATOMIC PHYSICS (8th edition), Max Born. Nobel laureate's lucid treatment of kinetic theory of gases, elementary particles, nuclear atom, wave-corpuscles, atomic structure and spectral lines, much more. Over 40 appendices, bibliography. 495pp. 5⅜ × 8½. 65984-4 Pa. $11.95

ELECTRONIC STRUCTURE AND THE PROPERTIES OF SOLIDS: The Physics of the Chemical Bond, Walter A. Harrison. Innovative text offers basic understanding of the electronic structure of covalent and ionic solids, simple metals, transition metals and their compounds. Problems. 1980 edition. 582pp. 6⅛ × 9¼. 66021-4 Pa. $14.95

BOUNDARY VALUE PROBLEMS OF HEAT CONDUCTION, M. Necati Özisik. Systematic, comprehensive treatment of modern mathematical methods of solving problems in heat conduction and diffusion. Numerous examples and problems. Selected references. Appendices. 505pp. 5⅜ × 8½. 65990-9 Pa. $11.95

A SHORT HISTORY OF CHEMISTRY (3rd edition), J.R. Partington. Classic exposition explores origins of chemistry, alchemy, early medical chemistry, nature of atmosphere, theory of valency, laws and structure of atomic theory, much more. 428pp. 5⅜ × 8½. (Available in U.S. only) 65977-1 Pa. $10.95

A HISTORY OF ASTRONOMY, A. Pannekoek. Well-balanced, carefully reasoned study covers such topics as Ptolemaic theory, work of Copernicus, Kepler, Newton, Eddington's work on stars, much more. Illustrated. References. 521pp. 5⅜ × 8½. 65994-1 Pa. $11.95

PRINCIPLES OF METEOROLOGICAL ANALYSIS, Walter J. Saucier. Highly respected, abundantly illustrated classic reviews atmospheric variables, hydrostatics, static stability, various analyses (scalar, cross-section, isobaric, isentropic, more). For intermediate meteorology students. 454pp. 6⅛ × 9¼. 65979-8 Pa. $12.95

RELATIVITY, THERMODYNAMICS AND COSMOLOGY, Richard C. Tolman. Landmark study extends thermodynamics to special, general relativity; also applications of relativistic mechanics, thermodynamics to cosmological models. 501pp. 5⅜ × 8½. 65383-8 Pa. $12.95

APPLIED ANALYSIS, Cornelius Lanczos. Classic work on analysis and design of finite processes for approximating solution of analytical problems. Algebraic equations, matrices, harmonic analysis, quadrature methods, much more. 559pp. 5⅜ × 8½. 65656-X Pa. $12.95

SPECIAL RELATIVITY FOR PHYSICISTS, G. Stephenson and C.W. Kilmister. Concise elegant account for nonspecialists. Lorentz transformation, optical and dynamical applications, more. Bibliography. 108pp. 5⅜ × 8½. 65519-9 Pa. $4.95

INTRODUCTION TO ANALYSIS, Maxwell Rosenlicht. Unusually clear, accessible coverage of set theory, real number system, metric spaces, continuous functions, Riemann integration, multiple integrals, more. Wide range of problems. Undergraduate level. Bibliography. 254pp. 5⅜ × 8½. 65038-3 Pa. $7.95

INTRODUCTION TO QUANTUM MECHANICS With Applications to Chemistry, Linus Pauling & E. Bright Wilson, Jr. Classic undergraduate text by Nobel Prize winner applies quantum mechanics to chemical and physical problems. Numerous tables and figures enhance the text. Chapter bibliographies. Appendices. Index. 468pp. 5⅜ × 8½. 64871-0 Pa. $11.95

ASYMPTOTIC EXPANSIONS OF INTEGRALS, Norman Bleistein & Richard A. Handelsman. Best introduction to important field with applications in a variety of scientific disciplines. New preface. Problems. Diagrams. Tables. Bibliography. Index. 448pp. 5⅜ × 8½. 65082-0 Pa. $11.95

MATHEMATICS APPLIED TO CONTINUUM MECHANICS, Lee A. Segel. Analyzes models of fluid flow and solid deformation. For upper-level math, science and engineering students. 608pp. 5⅜ × 8½. 65369-2 Pa. $13.95

ELEMENTS OF REAL ANALYSIS, David A. Sprecher. Classic text covers fundamental concepts, real number system, point sets, functions of a real variable, Fourier series, much more. Over 500 exercises. 352pp. 5⅜ × 8½. 65385-4 Pa. $9.95

PHYSICAL PRINCIPLES OF THE QUANTUM THEORY, Werner Heisenberg. Nobel Laureate discusses quantum theory, uncertainty, wave mechanics, work of Dirac, Schroedinger, Compton, Wilson, Einstein, etc. 184pp. 5⅜ × 8½. 60113-7 Pa. $4.95

INTRODUCTORY REAL ANALYSIS, A.N. Kolmogorov, S.V. Fomin. Translated by Richard A. Silverman. Self-contained, evenly paced introduction to real and functional analysis. Some 350 problems. 403pp. 5⅜ × 8½. 61226-0 Pa. $9.95

PROBLEMS AND SOLUTIONS IN QUANTUM CHEMISTRY AND PHYSICS, Charles S. Johnson, Jr. and Lee G. Pedersen. Unusually varied problems, detailed solutions in coverage of quantum mechanics, wave mechanics, angular momentum, molecular spectroscopy, scattering theory, more. 280 problems plus 139 supplementary exercises. 430pp. 6½ × 9¼. 65236-X Pa. $11.95

ASYMPTOTIC METHODS IN ANALYSIS, N.G. de Bruijn. An inexpensive, comprehensive guide to asymptotic methods—the pioneering work that teaches by explaining worked examples in detail. Index. 224pp. 5⅜ × 8½.   64221-6 Pa. $6.95

OPTICAL RESONANCE AND TWO-LEVEL ATOMS, L. Allen and J.H. Eberly. Clear, comprehensive introduction to basic principles behind all quantum optical resonance phenomena. 53 illustrations. Preface. Index. 256pp. 5⅜ × 8½.
65533-4 Pa. $7.95

COMPLEX VARIABLES, Francis J. Flanigan. Unusual approach, delaying complex algebra till harmonic functions have been analyzed from real variable viewpoint. Includes problems with answers. 364pp. 5⅜ × 8½.   61388-7 Pa. $7.95

ATOMIC SPECTRA AND ATOMIC STRUCTURE, Gerhard Herzberg. One of best introductions; especially for specialist in other fields. Treatment is physical rather than mathematical. 80 illustrations. 257pp. 5⅜ × 8½.   60115-3 Pa. $5.95

APPLIED COMPLEX VARIABLES, John W. Dettman. Step-by-step coverage of fundamentals of analytic function theory—plus lucid exposition of five important applications: Potential Theory; Ordinary Differential Equations; Fourier Transforms; Laplace Transforms; Asymptotic Expansions. 66 figures. Exercises at chapter ends. 512pp. 5⅜ × 8½.   64670-X Pa. $10.95

ULTRASONIC ABSORPTION: An Introduction to the Theory of Sound Absorption and Dispersion in Gases, Liquids and Solids, A.B. Bhatia. Standard reference in the field provides a clear, systematically organized introductory review of fundamental concepts for advanced graduate students, research workers. Numerous diagrams. Bibliography. 440pp. 5⅜ × 8½.   64917-2 Pa. $11.95

UNBOUNDED LINEAR OPERATORS: Theory and Applications, Seymour Goldberg. Classic presents systematic treatment of the theory of unbounded linear operators in normed linear spaces with applications to differential equations. Bibliography. 199pp. 5⅜ × 8½.   64830-3 Pa. $7.95

LIGHT SCATTERING BY SMALL PARTICLES, H.C. van de Hulst. Comprehensive treatment including full range of useful approximation methods for researchers in chemistry, meteorology and astronomy. 44 illustrations. 470pp. 5⅜ × 8½.   64228-3 Pa. $10.95

CONFORMAL MAPPING ON RIEMANN SURFACES, Harvey Cohn. Lucid, insightful book presents ideal coverage of subject. 334 exercises make book perfect for self-study. 55 figures. 352pp. 5⅜ × 8¼.   64025-6 Pa. $8.95

OPTICKS, Sir Isaac Newton. Newton's own experiments with spectroscopy, colors, lenses, reflection, refraction, etc., in language the layman can follow. Foreword by Albert Einstein. 532pp. 5⅜ × 8½.   60205-2 Pa. $9.95

GENERALIZED INTEGRAL TRANSFORMATIONS, A.H. Zemanian. Graduate-level study of recent generalizations of the Laplace, Mellin, Hankel, K. Weierstrass, convolution and other simple transformations. Bibliography. 320pp. 5⅜ × 8½.   65375-7 Pa. $7.95

THE ELECTROMAGNETIC FIELD, Albert Shadowitz. Comprehensive undergraduate text covers basics of electric and magnetic fields, builds up to electromagnetic theory. Also related topics, including relativity. Over 900 problems. 768pp. 5⅜ × 8¼. 65660-8 Pa. $17.95

FOURIER SERIES, Georgi P. Tolstov. Translated by Richard A. Silverman. A valuable addition to the literature on the subject, moving clearly from subject to subject and theorem to theorem. 107 problems, answers. 336pp. 5⅜ × 8½. 63317-9 Pa. $7.95

THEORY OF ELECTROMAGNETIC WAVE PROPAGATION, Charles Herach Papas. Graduate-level study discusses the Maxwell field equations, radiation from wire antennas, the Doppler effect and more. xiii + 244pp. 5⅜ × 8½. 65678-0 Pa. $6.95

DISTRIBUTION THEORY AND TRANSFORM ANALYSIS: An Introduction to Generalized Functions, with Applications, A.H. Zemanian. Provides basics of distribution theory, describes generalized Fourier and Laplace transformations. Numerous problems. 384pp. 5⅜ × 8½. 65479-6 Pa. $9.95

THE PHYSICS OF WAVES, William C. Elmore and Mark A. Heald. Unique overview of classical wave theory. Acoustics, optics, electromagnetic radiation, more. Ideal as classroom text or for self-study. Problems. 477pp. 5⅜ × 8½. 64926-1 Pa. $11.95

CALCULUS OF VARIATIONS WITH APPLICATIONS, George M. Ewing. Applications-oriented introduction to variational theory develops insight and promotes understanding of specialized books, research papers. Suitable for advanced undergraduate/graduate students as primary, supplementary text. 352pp. 5⅜ × 8½. 64856-7 Pa. $8.95

A TREATISE ON ELECTRICITY AND MAGNETISM, James Clerk Maxwell. Important foundation work of modern physics. Brings to final form Maxwell's theory of electromagnetism and rigorously derives his general equations of field theory. 1,084pp. 5⅜ × 8½. 60636-8, 60637-6 Pa., Two-vol. set $19.90

AN INTRODUCTION TO THE CALCULUS OF VARIATIONS, Charles Fox. Graduate-level text covers variations of an integral, isoperimetrical problems, least action, special relativity, approximations, more. References. 279pp. 5⅜ × 8½. 65499-0 Pa. $7.95

HYDRODYNAMIC AND HYDROMAGNETIC STABILITY, S. Chandrasekhar. Lucid examination of the Rayleigh-Benard problem; clear coverage of the theory of instabilities causing convection. 704pp. 5⅜ × 8¼. 64071-X Pa. $14.95

CALCULUS OF VARIATIONS, Robert Weinstock. Basic introduction covering isoperimetric problems, theory of elasticity, quantum mechanics, electrostatics, etc. Exercises throughout. 326pp. 5⅜ × 8½. 63069-2 Pa. $7.95

DYNAMICS OF FLUIDS IN POROUS MEDIA, Jacob Bear. For advanced students of ground water hydrology, soil mechanics and physics, drainage and irrigation engineering and more. 335 illustrations. Exercises, with answers. 784pp. 6⅛ × 9¼. 65675-6 Pa. $19.95

NUMERICAL METHODS FOR SCIENTISTS AND ENGINEERS, Richard Hamming. Classic text stresses frequency approach in coverage of algorithms, polynomial approximation, Fourier approximation, exponential approximation, other topics. Revised and enlarged 2nd edition. 721pp. 5⅜ × 8½.
65241-6 Pa. $14.95

THEORETICAL SOLID STATE PHYSICS, Vol. I: Perfect Lattices in Equilibrium; Vol. II: Non-Equilibrium and Disorder, William Jones and Norman H. March. Monumental reference work covers fundamental theory of equilibrium properties of perfect crystalline solids, non-equilibrium properties, defects and disordered systems. Appendices. Problems. Preface. Diagrams. Index. Bibliography. Total of 1,301pp. 5⅜ × 8½. Two volumes. Vol. I 65015-4 Pa. $12.95
Vol. II 65016-2 Pa. $12.95

OPTIMIZATION THEORY WITH APPLICATIONS, Donald A. Pierre. Broad-spectrum approach to important topic. Classical theory of minima and maxima, calculus of variations, simplex technique and linear programming, more. Many problems, examples. 640pp. 5⅜ × 8½. 65205-X Pa. $13.95

THE MODERN THEORY OF SOLIDS, Frederick Seitz. First inexpensive edition of classic work on theory of ionic crystals, free-electron theory of metals and semiconductors, molecular binding, much more. 736pp. 5⅜ × 8½.
65482-6 Pa. $15.95

ESSAYS ON THE THEORY OF NUMBERS, Richard Dedekind. Two classic essays by great German mathematician: on the theory of irrational numbers; and on transfinite numbers and properties of natural numbers. 115pp. 5⅜ × 8½.
21010-3 Pa. $4.95

THE FUNCTIONS OF MATHEMATICAL PHYSICS, Harry Hochstadt. Comprehensive treatment of orthogonal polynomials, hypergeometric functions, Hill's equation, much more. Bibliography. Index. 322pp. 5⅜ × 8½. 65214-9 Pa. $9.95

NUMBER THEORY AND ITS HISTORY, Oystein Ore. Unusually clear, accessible introduction covers counting, properties of numbers, prime numbers, much more. Bibliography. 380pp. 5⅜ × 8½. 65620-9 Pa. $8.95

THE VARIATIONAL PRINCIPLES OF MECHANICS, Cornelius Lanczos. Graduate level coverage of calculus of variations, equations of motion, relativistic mechanics, more. First inexpensive paperbound edition of classic treatise. Index. Bibliography. 418pp. 5⅜ × 8½. 65067-7 Pa. $10.95

MATHEMATICAL TABLES AND FORMULAS, Robert D. Carmichael and Edwin R. Smith. Logarithms, sines, tangents, trig functions, powers, roots, reciprocals, exponential and hyperbolic functions, formulas and theorems. 269pp. 5⅜ × 8½. 60111-0 Pa. $5.95

THEORETICAL PHYSICS, Georg Joos, with Ira M. Freeman. Classic overview covers essential math, mechanics, electromagnetic theory, thermodynamics, quantum mechanics, nuclear physics, other topics. First paperback edition. xxiii + 885pp. 5⅜ × 8½. 65227-0 Pa. $18.95

HANDBOOK OF MATHEMATICAL FUNCTIONS WITH FORMULAS, GRAPHS, AND MATHEMATICAL TABLES, edited by Milton Abramowitz and Irene A. Stegun. Vast compendium: 29 sets of tables, some to as high as 20 places. 1,046pp. 8 × 10½. 61272-4 Pa. $22.95

MATHEMATICAL METHODS IN PHYSICS AND ENGINEERING, John W. Dettman. Algebraically based approach to vectors, mapping, diffraction, other topics in applied math. Also generalized functions, analytic function theory, more. Exercises. 448pp. 5⅜ × 8¼. 65649-7 Pa. $8.95

A SURVEY OF NUMERICAL MATHEMATICS, David M. Young and Robert Todd Gregory. Broad self-contained coverage of computer-oriented numerical algorithms for solving various types of mathematical problems in linear algebra, ordinary and partial, differential equations, much more. Exercises. Total of 1,248pp. 5⅜ × 8½. Two volumes. Vol. I 65691-8 Pa. $14.95
Vol. II 65692-6 Pa. $14.95

TENSOR ANALYSIS FOR PHYSICISTS, J.A. Schouten. Concise exposition of the mathematical basis of tensor analysis, integrated with well-chosen physical examples of the theory. Exercises. Index. Bibliography. 289pp. 5⅜ × 8½. 65582-2 Pa. $7.95

INTRODUCTION TO NUMERICAL ANALYSIS (2nd Edition), F.B. Hildebrand. Classic, fundamental treatment covers computation, approximation, interpolation, numerical differentiation and integration, other topics. 150 new problems. 669pp. 5⅜ × 8½. 65363-3 Pa. $14.95

INVESTIGATIONS ON THE THEORY OF THE BROWNIAN MOVEMENT, Albert Einstein. Five papers (1905–8) investigating dynamics of Brownian motion and evolving elementary theory. Notes by R. Fürth. 122pp. 5⅜ × 8½. 60304-0 Pa. $4.95

NUMERICAL METHODS FOR SCIENTISTS AND ENGINEERS, Richard Hamming. Classic text stresses frequency approach in coverage of algorithms, polynomial approximation, Fourier approximation, exponential approximation, other topics. Revised and enlarged 2nd edition. 721pp. 5⅜ × 8½. 65241-6 Pa. $14.95

AN INTRODUCTION TO STATISTICAL THERMODYNAMICS, Terrell L. Hill. Excellent basic text offers wide-ranging coverage of quantum statistical mechanics, systems of interacting molecules, quantum statistics, more. 523pp. 5⅜ × 8½. 65242-4 Pa. $11.95

ELEMENTARY DIFFERENTIAL EQUATIONS, William Ted Martin and Eric Reissner. Exceptionally clear, comprehensive introduction at undergraduate level. Nature and origin of differential equations, differential equations of first, second and higher orders. Picard's Theorem, much more. Problems with solutions. 331pp. 5⅜ × 8½. 65024-3 Pa. $8.95

STATISTICAL PHYSICS, Gregory H. Wannier. Classic text combines thermodynamics, statistical mechanics and kinetic theory in one unified presentation of thermal physics. Problems with solutions. Bibliography. 532pp. 5⅜ × 8½. 65401-X Pa. $11.95

ORDINARY DIFFERENTIAL EQUATIONS, Morris Tenenbaum and Harry Pollard. Exhaustive survey of ordinary differential equations for undergraduates in mathematics, engineering, science. Thorough analysis of theorems. Diagrams. Bibliography. Index. 818pp. 5⅜ × 8½. 64940-7 Pa. $16.95

STATISTICAL MECHANICS: Principles and Applications, Terrell L. Hill. Standard text covers fundamentals of statistical mechanics, applications to fluctuation theory, imperfect gases, distribution functions, more. 448pp. 5⅜ × 8½. 65390-0 Pa. $9.95

ORDINARY DIFFERENTIAL EQUATIONS AND STABILITY THEORY: An Introduction, David A. Sánchez. Brief, modern treatment. Linear equation, stability theory for autonomous and nonautonomous systems, etc. 164pp. 5⅜ × 8¼. 63828-6 Pa. $5.95

THIRTY YEARS THAT SHOOK PHYSICS: The Story of Quantum Theory, George Gamow. Lucid, accessible introduction to influential theory of energy and matter. Careful explanations of Dirac's anti-particles, Bohr's model of the atom, much more. 12 plates. Numerous drawings. 240pp. 5⅜ × 8½. 24895-X Pa. $5.95

THEORY OF MATRICES, Sam Perlis. Outstanding text covering rank, nonsingularity and inverses in connection with the development of canonical matrices under the relation of equivalence, and without the intervention of determinants. Includes exercises. 237pp. 5⅜ × 8½. 66810-X Pa. $7.95

GREAT EXPERIMENTS IN PHYSICS: Firsthand Accounts from Galileo to Einstein, edited by Morris H. Shamos. 25 crucial discoveries: Newton's laws of motion, Chadwick's study of the neutron, Hertz on electromagnetic waves, more. Original accounts clearly annotated. 370pp. 5⅜ × 8½. 25346-5 Pa. $9.95

INTRODUCTION TO PARTIAL DIFFERENTIAL EQUATIONS WITH APPLICATIONS, E.C. Zachmanoglou and Dale W. Thoe. Essentials of partial differential equations applied to common problems in engineering and the physical sciences. Problems and answers. 416pp. 5⅜ × 8½. 65251-3 Pa. $10.95

BURNHAM'S CELESTIAL HANDBOOK, Robert Burnham, Jr. Thorough guide to the stars beyond our solar system. Exhaustive treatment. Alphabetical by constellation: Andromeda to Cetus in Vol. 1; Chamaeleon to Orion in Vol. 2; and Pavo to Vulpecula in Vol. 3. Hundreds of illustrations. Index in Vol. 3. 2,000pp. 6⅛ × 9¼. 23567-X, 23568-8, 23673-0 Pa., Three-vol. set $41.85

ASYMPTOTIC EXPANSIONS FOR ORDINARY DIFFERENTIAL EQUATIONS, Wolfgang Wasow. Outstanding text covers asymptotic power series, Jordan's canonical form, turning point problems, singular perturbations, much more. Problems. 384pp. 5⅜ × 8½. 65456-7 Pa. $9.95

AMATEUR ASTRONOMER'S HANDBOOK, J.B. Sidgwick. Timeless, comprehensive coverage of telescopes, mirrors, lenses, mountings, telescope drives, micrometers, spectroscopes, more. 189 illustrations. 576pp. 5⅜ × 8¼. (USO) 24034-7 Pa. $9.95

CHALLENGING MATHEMATICAL PROBLEMS WITH ELEMENTARY SOLUTIONS, A.M. Yaglom and I.M. Yaglom. Over 170 challenging problems on probability theory, combinatorial analysis, points and lines, topology, convex polygons, many other topics. Solutions. Total of 445pp. 5⅜ × 8½. Two-vol. set.
Vol. I 65536-9 Pa. $6.95
Vol. II 65537-7 Pa. $6.95

FIFTY CHALLENGING PROBLEMS IN PROBABILITY WITH SOLUTIONS, Frederick Mosteller. Remarkable puzzlers, graded in difficulty, illustrate elementary and advanced aspects of probability. Detailed solutions. 88pp. 5⅜ × 8½.
65355-2 Pa. $3.95

EXPERIMENTS IN TOPOLOGY, Stephen Barr. Classic, lively explanation of one of the byways of mathematics. Klein bottles, Moebius strips, projective planes, map coloring, problem of the Koenigsberg bridges, much more, described with clarity and wit. 43 figures. 210pp. 5⅜ × 8½.
25933-1 Pa. $5.95

RELATIVITY IN ILLUSTRATIONS, Jacob T. Schwartz. Clear nontechnical treatment makes relativity more accessible than ever before. Over 60 drawings illustrate concepts more clearly than text alone. Only high school geometry needed. Bibliography. 128pp. 6⅛ × 9¼.
25965-X Pa. $5.95

AN INTRODUCTION TO ORDINARY DIFFERENTIAL EQUATIONS, Earl A. Coddington. A thorough and systematic first course in elementary differential equations for undergraduates in mathematics and science, with many exercises and problems (with answers). Index. 304pp. 5⅜ × 8½.
65942-9 Pa. $7.95

FOURIER SERIES AND ORTHOGONAL FUNCTIONS, Harry F. Davis. An incisive text combining theory and practical example to introduce Fourier series, orthogonal functions and applications of the Fourier method to boundary-value problems. 570 exercises. Answers and notes. 416pp. 5⅜ × 8½.
65973-9 Pa. $9.95

THE THEORY OF BRANCHING PROCESSES, Theodore E. Harris. First systematic, comprehensive treatment of branching (i.e. multiplicative) processes and their applications. Galton-Watson model, Markov branching processes, electron-photon cascade, many other topics. Rigorous proofs. Bibliography. 240pp. 5⅜ × 8½.
65952-6 Pa. $6.95

AN INTRODUCTION TO ALGEBRAIC STRUCTURES, Joseph Landin. Superb self-contained text covers "abstract algebra": sets and numbers, theory of groups, theory of rings, much more. Numerous well-chosen examples, exercises. 247pp. 5⅜ × 8½.
65940-2 Pa. $6.95

Prices subject to change without notice.
Available at your book dealer or write for free Mathematics and Science Catalog to Dept. GI, Dover Publications, Inc., 31 East 2nd St., Mineola, N.Y. 11501. Dover publishes more than 175 books each year on science, elementary and advanced mathematics, biology, music, art, literature, history, social sciences and other areas.